The New Optimists

Scientists View Tomorrow's World
& What It Means To Us

Edited by **Keith Richards**

with a foreword by **Jenny Uglow**

LINUS
PUBLISHING

Linus Publishing Company Limited
The Moseley Exchange
149-153 Alcester Road
Birmingham
B13 8JP

www.newoptimists.com

A CIP Catalogue record for this book is available from the British Library.

ISBN 978-1-907843-00-6

Typeset by Etica Press Ltd, Malvern, Worcestershire WR14 1ET

Printed and bound in Great Britain by Thomson Litho Ltd, East Kilbride, Scotland

Foreword

Jenny Uglow

The New Optimists is the most exhilarating of books. It looks to the future, not through rose-tinted glasses, but with a clear vision, aware of difficulties and challenges yet convinced that research and experiment can help the human race to overcome them. It seems entirely right that scientists should step forth and speak out in this way, on the 350th anniversary of the founding of the Royal Society. Right too that the 2010 meeting of the British Science Association should be held in Birmingham, a place that has always been a town of forges and anvils, of making and invention, a crucible of ideas.

In 1660, the men who gathered at Gresham College in London, determined to explore the universe they inhabited, decided to form a society to enjoy, said their historian Thomas Sprat, 'the satisfaction of breathing a freer air, and of conversation in quiet with one with another, without being engaged in the passions, and madness of that dismal age'. In Birmingham, that spirit was continued a century later in the men of the Lunar Society, among them James Watt and Matthew Boulton, Erasmus Darwin, Josiah Wedgwood, Joseph Priestley and the chemist James Keir. Their interests ranged from astronomy, optics and electricity to chemistry, engineering and metallurgy, and to medicine and botany, and their long collaboration brought together their different experiences and skills, providing lifelong support. They too looked to the future, setting aside political differences, and concerned above all to make the world a better place.

The current collection of short essays – brief answers to the question *'What are you optimistic about?'* – is itself a kind of conversation. In the great tradition of the Royal Society it brings together an extensive range of specialists from the region, free from political agendas or mercenary aims. And just as the original Lunar Men felt they were changing their world, so these men and women are changing ours, and collectively they have far more impact than individually.

The list of contributors is dizzying. The majority work in medicine and life-sciences, the region's great strength. But they share this book with engineers, chemists, computer and digital media scientists, environmental and energy experts and the wilder shores of research into games programming or forensic linguistics. The topics covered are therefore varied and wide-ranging, from cell memory and genome sequencing to urban ecosystems, from vital ways to reduce carbon emissions to crop rotation and even the notion of 'happiness'. And while 'optimism' is a term that implies application, the importance of pure research becomes increasingly clear.

The future that is unveiled can also induce vertigo. It is extraordinary to think that people may live to be 1000, or that 'we are about to enter an age when having a copy of one's own genome sequence is as common as carrying a mobile phone is today'. Scientists, it seems, are often visionaries. All these essays are imbued with a driving spirit of curiosity, combined with energetic analysis, and often with passion. Yet the most idealistic, or imaginative scenarios also coexist with a realistic toughness – a recognition that solving one set of problems, like improvements in health, can lead to others, like the challenges of ageing. That particular theme evokes a typical variety of response, with some contributions dealing with specific problems like 'renewing' eyes, while others play with scary ideas of neurocognitive prostheses – or cheerier ones like the benefit of taking up the tango.

The issues are serious, but the answers will often make you laugh. All the writers convey their own excitement in their work, and we are privileged that this fascinating collection allows us to share it. New researchers and old hands all have their say, making no bones about the need for persistence, the long hours in the lab and the frequent frustrations. For some, the rare moments of revelation make everything worthwhile. For others, the greatest pleasure comes from slow, fruitful collaboration. No one here feels that their research is conclusive, or that final discoveries can be made. Like the early scientists, and the men of the Lunar Society, they are still voyagers, standing on the shore looking out towards misty horizons. There will always be new questions to answer – and this in itself is a cause for optimism.

Contents

contents

Chapter 2: Changing bodies

contents

Part 2: The Macrocosm – Interacting with our world

Chapter 3: Living in the natural world

Chapter 4: Living in the virtual world

contents

Part 3: Transformations

Chapter 5: Getting to the heart of things

contents

contents

Part 4: The ways of science

Chapter 7: Working together

contents

Chapter 8: Thinking differently

Chapter 9: From where I stand

contents

The Contributors

Derek Alderson

Professor Derek Alderson holds the Baring Chair of Surgery at the University of Birmingham. Current Editor of the *British Journal of Surgery*, his main area of clinical interest is in oesophago-gastric surgery.

Graham Anderson

Professor Graham Anderson works in the Department of Immunity and Infection at the University of Birmingham. His main area of research is the spectrum of antigens recognised by the peripheral T-cell population; ie the ability of discriminate self from non-self.

Hazel Barrett

Professor Hazel Barrett is Head of Department at Coventry University's Department of Geography, Environment and Disaster Management. Her current research interests are in health and poverty in the developing world, including HIV/AIDS and children in sub-Saharan Africa.

Lucy Bastin

Dr Lucy Bastin is a lecturer in GIS (Geographical Information Systems) at Aston University. She applies spatial analysis techniques to health, environmental and socio-demographic research challenges. She started out working for the Birmingham Urban Wildlife Trust, and then studied for a BSc in Zoology (Nottingham) and a PhD in the population ecology of urban plants (Birmingham). She has also worked as a researcher on fuzzy classifications of satellite imagery, and spent several years as a senior software developer at Tadpole-Cartesia.

Russell Beale

Dr Russell Beale leads the Advanced Interaction Group in the School of Computer Science at the University of Birmingham. His research focus is on using intelligence to support user interaction. As well as being a full-time academic, Russell has founded four companies and run two of them, provides consultancy services on projects he's interested in, and used to race yachts competitively until a toddler and infant twins needed his attention – but once they've learned to sail, he'll return to that as well.

Robert Berry

Professor Robert Berry joined Aston University as Dean of the School of Engineering and Applied Science in 2008. Before this, he was IBM Distinguished Engineer with IBM UK in Hursley, Hampshire. His research interests lie in developing techniques for understanding and improving the performance of large complex software systems.

Roslyn Bill

Dr Roslyn Bill is Reader in Molecular Biosciences at Aston University. She has worked in the US (as a Fullbright Scholar) and Sweden as well as the UK. Her research interests are in understanding the molecular features defining successful protein production in yeasts, with an emphasis on membrane proteins such as water and glycerol channels, tetraspanins and G protein-coupled receptors. Many of these membrane proteins are potential drug targets. Her work is funded by EPSRC, BBSRC and the European Commission and she has worked in collaboration with industrial partners throughout her career, as her research is central to progress in the drug discovery pipeline.

Tony Bridgwater

Tony Bridgwater is Professor of Chemical Engineering at Aston University, where he leads the Bioenergy Research Group (BERG). His current research interests are on the development of technologies for fast pyrolysis of biomass, and the production of biofuels and chemical products that can be derived from biomass and from the fast pyrolysis liquids. He is Technical Director of the SUPERGEN Bioenergy Consortium supported by the EPSRC, and contributes to several EC-sponsored research projects including Dibanet, Biosynergy, Bioenergy Network of Excellence, Bioliquids CHP and Bioref-Integ. He was awarded the European Johannes Linneborn Prize in 2007 for his outstanding contribution to developing energy from biomass, and the North American Don Klass Award for Excellence in Thermochemical Science in 2009.

Gordon Brown

Gordon Brown is a Professor in the Psychology Department at Warwick University. His research interests include human timing and memory, word recognition, and rank-based effects in judgement, decision-making, and economic and psychological science. (co-authors Neil Stewart and Alex Wood)

Chris Buckley

Chris Buckley received his MBBS from the University of London in 1990, having obtained a degree in Biochemistry from the University of Oxford in 1985. He trained in rheumatology at the Hammersmith Hospital London with Mark Walport and Dorian Haskard and then completed a D Phil with David Simmons at the Institute of Molecular Medicine Oxford in 1996. He then moved to the Rheumatology Unit in Birmingham as a Wellcome Trust Clinician Scientist and in 2001 was appointed as MRC Senior Clinical Fellow in the Division of Immunity and Infection at the MRC Centre for Immune Regulation. He was appointed Professor of Rheumatology in 2002. Professor Buckley's current research focus is an analysis of mechanisms of leukocyte accumulation in chronic inflammation. (co-authors Andrew Filer and Karim Raza)

Tim Bugg

Tim Bugg is Professor of Biological Chemistry at Warwick University. His research interests are the understanding of important enzyme-catalysed reactions, using a combination of the following techniques: synthesis of enzymatic substrates and inhibitors, isotope labelling experiments, enzyme purification and enzyme kinetics. Major areas of interest are enzymes involved in the bacterial degradation of aromatic compounds, and enzymes involved in bacterial cell wall peptidoglycan biosynthesis, as targets for the development of novel antibacterial agents.

David Burden

David Burden is a Chartered and European Engineer. His career started in army communications managing a range of mobile and wireless systems before joining Ascom, a Swiss telecomms company and then Aseriti, the IT arm of Severn Trent plc. During the dot com boom, he founded a wireless data company developing both WAP and Voice XML systems. In 2004, he set up Daden Ltd, a virtual worlds and information 2.0 consultancy.

Rebecca Cain

Dr Rebecca Cain is Assistant Professor in Experiential Engineering at the Warwick Manufacturing Group (part of the School of Engineering) of the University of Warwick. Originally trained as an industrial designer, she now works across multi-disciplinary teams to connect engineering to real people. Her research interests are in how humans' subjective reactions to products and environments can be communicated in a meaningful way to scientists and engineers. Applications from her research are in urban soundscapes, automotive design and healthcare environment design.

Gemma Calvert

Professor Gemma Calvert is the Chair of Applied Neuroimaging at the Warwick Manufacturing Group. She began her career in the marketing and advertising industry, working for FKB-Carison (1987–91) before returning to academe. She has a Bachelors degree in Psychology from the LSE, and DPhil in Functional Brain Imaging from the University of Oxford where she subsequently established and directed a specialist neuroimaging lab until 2004. Her unique career path led her to found the world's first neuromarketing company, Neurosense Limited, in 1999 and she has over 15 years' experience in the commercial application of modern brain imaging methods for marketing and manufacturing.

David Chandler

Dr Dave Chandler is Senior Research Scientist at the Horticultural Research International, part of the University of Warwick. A microbiologist and entomologist, he conducts research into invertebrate microbial interactions. His main areas of interest are biological pest control, integrated pest management and bee health. He is a Fellow of the Royal Entomological Society, and sits of the editorial advisory boards for Biocontrol Science and Biological Control. He is also a member of the biocontrol group of the Association of Applied Biologists, and a Council Member of the Society for Invertebrate Pathology.

Jackie Chappell

Dr Jackie Chappell is Lecturer in Animal Behaviour at the Centre for Ornithology in the School of Biosciences at the University of Birmingham. She spent several years at the University of Oxford studying various aspects of animal cognition, including tool use in New Caledonian crows. Since moving to the University of Birmingham in 2004, her interests have broadened to the study of cognitive adaptations: how do animals use intelligence to adapt to their environment, and why do only some species use this strategy?

Iain Chapple

Iain Chapple is Professor and Head of Periodontology and Consultant in Restorative Dentistry at Birmingham Dental School. He leads a Periodontal Research team active in the investigation of the pathobiological aspects of periodontal disease and mechanistic links between periodontal inflammation and systemic inflammatory diseases. He has a strong interest in free radical and antioxidant biology. (co-author Tony Smith)

Susanne Charlesworth

Dr Sue Charlesworth is Reader in Urban Geography at Coventry University. She began her career as a Medical Laboratory Technician, then took an OU degree followed by a PhD investigating the sediments collecting in urban lakes and rivers. This began her research interest in sustainable drainage (SUDS), an applied multidisciplinary area of work involving engineers, town planners, social scientists, ecologists and pure scientists.

Juliet Coates

Dr Juliet Coates teaches and runs a research group in the School of Biosciences at Birmingham University. She is interested in the development and evolution of many-celled organisms. In her research group, they try to understand at the molecular level how plant cells integrate information to form a many-celled plant with specific tissues and a certain form. They focus particularly on the development of the root system, and certain families of proteins that control it. They also study 'ancient' land plants that they hope will tell us more about how more complex plants evolved. They collaborate with other research groups that work on root development and with groups that study relatives of our plant proteins that control the life cycle of the malaria parasite.

Jack Cohen

Dr Jack Cohen is Hon Professor of Mathematics at Warwick University, and a Fellow of the Institute of Biology. A now-retired reproductive biologist, he published widely in academic journals. He has also written several books, and co-authored *Collapse of Chaos and Figments of Reality* with Professor Ian Stewart with whom he has also written several science fiction novels. Cohen and Stewart teamed with Terry Pratchett to write three Science of Discworld books.

Barbara Conway

Dr Barbara Conway is Senior Lecturer in Pharmaceutics at Aston University. Her research interests are in the optimisation of delivery profiles using formulation design to improve solubility and dissolution profiles, bioavailability, drug stability, kietics and in-vitro–in-vivo correlations.

Charles Craddock

Charles Craddock is Professor of Heamatolo-oncology at the University of Birmingham, and Director of the Blood and Marrow Transplant Unit at the University Hospital Birmingham NHS Foundation Trust. He has particular interest in the development of novel transplant and drug therapies in leukaemia and myeloma. He also works with groups researching chromatin structure in acute-myeloid leukaemia, mechanisms of drug resistance in myeloma and characterisation of dysregulated signalling pathways in leukaemia using proteomics.

Rachel Edwards

Dr Rachel Edwards is Assistant Professor in the Department of Physics at Warwick University. Her main research interests are in non-contact generation and detection of ultrasound using lasers and electromagnatic acoustic transducers, with applications in non-destructive testing and in low temperature measurements of phase changes in single crystals. She was a NESTA–Crucible awardee in 2007, and holds an ERC Starting Independent Researcher Grant.

Andrew Filer

Dr Andrew Filer is Senior Lecturer at the University of Birmingham and a Consultant Rheumatologist at Sandwell and West Birmingham Hospitals NHS Trust. His research interests focus on the mechanisms underlying inflammation in patients with early arthritis. He is also a fully-trained musculoskeletal sonographer and his other area of research interest is using ultrasound to image the joints of patients with early arthritis. (co authors Chris Buckley and Karim Raza)

Jeremy Foss

Jerry Foss is a lecturer involved in research at Birmingham City University. His subject areas include digital media technologies and their markets, including media distribution, interactive TV and serious virtual worlds. He is also a guest lecturer at other UK and European universities. He has 30 years' industry experience with GEC, GPT and Marconi Communications in distributed computing, broadband development (including IPTV triple play services), network strategy, intelligent agents and collaborative virtual environments.

Jon Frampton

Jon Frampton is presently the Professor of Stem Cell Biology and Director of the Stem Cell Centre at the University of Birmingham. Previously, he ran research groups in the European Molecular Biology Laboratory in Heidelberg (1988–95) and the Weatherall Institute of Molecular Medicine at the University of Oxford (1995–2002). His major research interests focus on the regulation of stem cell behaviour in health and disease. In particular, he is interested in blood stem cells, both normal and those related to leukaemia, although other studies encompass a number of adult stem cell types (eg those giving rise to bone and fat and the resident stem cells in the heart).

Jayne Franklyn

Jayne Franklyn is an endocrinologist, specialising in thyroid disease. A Professor of Medicine at the University of Birmingham and the Queen Elizabeth Hospital, she is also President of the British Thyroid Association.

David French

David French is Professor of Health Psychology at Coventry University. His main research areas are in the development and evaluation of interventions to change health-related behaviours, especially walking, and risk communication, especially the cognitive, emotional and behavioural effects of screening programmes.

Miriam Gifford

Dr Miriam L Gifford is an Assistant Professor at Warwick HRI/Warwick Systems Biology. Her research uses bioinformatic and cell-specific genomic techniques to understand how specialised cells in the root function to enable plants to cope with nitrogen limitation in the environment. Current research in the lab is using comparative genomics to compare environmental responses in the legume Medicago truncatula to the non-legume Arabidopsis thaliana at the cell-type level to gain insight into the evolutionary origin of nodulation.

Tim Grant

Dr Tim Grant is Deputy Director of the Centre for Forensic Linguistics at Aston University. His consultancy primarily involves authorship analysis and he has worked in many different contexts including investigations into sexual assault, murder and terrorist offences. He publishes on forensic linguistics and forensic psychology and his research into text messaging analysis was awarded the 2008 Joseph Lister Prize by the British Science Association. He considers himself a natural optimist.

Laura Green

Professor Laura Green is an epidemiologist in the Department of Biological Sciences at Warwick University. She leads multidisciplinary teams to reduce the clinical impact of endemic infectious diseases of farmed animals. Of current interest are three research projects on the control of footrot in sheep. One combines laboratory studies of persistence of D. nodosus, the causal organism, and mathematical modelling of persistence, one is investigating a novel approach to treatment and control in a clinical trial and one is on technology transfer to the sheep industry.

Richard Green

Richard Green is Professor of Energy Economics at the University of Birmingham, and is Director of its Institute for Energy Research and Policy. His main research interests are in the economics and regulation of the electricity industry and energy policy.

Helen Griffiths

Helen Griffiths is Executive Dean at Aston University, where she is Professor in Biomedical Sciences and founding director of Aston Research Centre for Healthy Ageing. Her research interests are proteomic approaches to biomarker determination and the interplay between lipids/sphingolipids and reactive oxygen species in inflammation and ageing. She also won the first Catherine Pasquier Prize from the European Society for Free Radical Research, and the Aston Excellence Award 2009 for Outstanding Researcher of the Year.

Anthony Hilton

Dr Anthony Hilton is Reader in Microbiology at Aston University. His current research group is working on projects including the molecular epidemiology of hospital and community MRSA, phenotypic and genotypic characterisation of Clostridium difficile, the role of flying insects in the spread of hospital-associated pathogens and Salmonella carriage in companion animals. In addition, he is involved in the public engagement with microbiology, including the BBC series *Grime Scene Investigation* and *The One Show*. In 2009, he received the Society for Applied Microbiology Communication Award and the Aston Excellence Award for his contribution to community engagement.

Garry Homer

Dr Garry Homer is Technical Director of the IT Futures Centre the e-Innovation Centre at the University of Wolverhampton. He specialises in industry-based R&D projects.

Andreas Hornung

Professor Andreas Hornung holds the Chair in Chemical Engineering and Applied Chemistry at Aston University where he is also Head of the European Bioenergy Research Institute as well as the Chemical Engineering and Applied Chemistry Group. His major research interests are in pyrolysis processes from micro-scale to technical application, and the thermo-chemical treatment of biomass.

David Hukins

David Hukins is Professor of Biomedical Engineering and Head of School of Mechanical Engineering at the University of Birmingham. His research interests are in the structure, function, failure, replacement and repair of tissues and parts of the body.

Craig Jackson

Craig Jackson is Head of the Psychology Division and Professor of Occupational Health Psychology at Birmingham City University. His main research interests are in how workplaces and working affect people's health and psychological well-being. He has specific interest in unusual and rare occupations, work-related suicide, and emerging issues such as technology change, workplace cultures and new working practices. He maintains a research interest in some of the traditional issues such as pesticides, metal and chemical exposures, and working hours.

Nicholas James

Nick James is Professor of Clinical Oncology at the University of Birmingham and the Queen Elizabeth Hospital. He qualified from St Bartholomew's Hospital with the principal class prize in medicine. After general training in London and Brussels, oncology training was undertaken at Hammersmith, the Royal Marsden, St Mary's and St Bartholomew's Hospitals and at the Cancer Institute, Tokyo. His current research is focussed on urological tumours and he is lead investigator on a number of international trials. In 1994 he co-founded the leading patient website CancerHelp UK (www.cancerhelp.org.uk), which has won numerous awards.

Philip Johnson

Philip Johnson is Professor of Oncology and Translational Research and Director of the Cancer Research UK Clinical Trials Unit at the University of Birmingham. He developed his interest in clinical trials and hepatobiliary cancer whilst at the Institute of Liver Studies, King's College Hospital, London, where he subsequently became Assistant Director. In 1992 he was appointed to the Chair of Clinical Oncology at the Chinese University of Hong Kong where he also became Director of the Cancer Centre and developed the Comprehensive Clinical Trials Unit whilst furthering his research interests into molecular biomarkers of cancer and new approaches to treatment of liver cancer.

David Jones

David Jones is Emeritus Professor of Sport and Exercise Science at the University of Birmingham and Emeritus Professor of Muscle Physiology at Manchester Metropolitan University. With a first degree in Medical Biochemistry from Birmingham and a PhD from the Institute of Psychiatry in London, his first professional contact with muscle and exercise came at the Postgraduate Medical Centre at Hammersmith with work on the biochemistry and physiology of fatigue. Current interests are fatigue during exercise (with applications for both improving athletic performance and helping patients with exercise intolerance) and the stimulus for muscle growth with, too, an interest in the genetic basis for differences in the response to training between subjects.

Deirdre Kelly

Professor Deirdre Kelly is a graduate of Trinity College, Dublin and is a Professor of Paediatric Hepatology. She has trained in both adult and paediatric gastroenterology and hepatology. She set up the Paediatric Liver Unit at Birmingham Children's Hospital, which provides a national and international service for children with liver failure and undergoing liver transplantation, transforming survival and outcome for these children. Until 2008, the Unit was the only national unit to be designated for small bowel and liver transplantation in the UK. She runs an active research programme focussing on viral hepatitis in children, molecular biology and genetics of inherited liver disease, quality and outcome of life following liver and/or intestinal transplantation. She is a Commissioner on the Care Quality Commission (2008–). She is currently President of the European Society of Paediatric Gastroenterology, Hepatology and Nutrition (ESPGHAN). She was Chairman of the Lunar Society (2007–09).

Julia King

Professor Julia King is Vice-Chancellor of Aston University. An engineer with over 160 published papers on fatigue and fracture in structural materials and developments in aerospace and marine propulsion technology, she has held a number of senior posts both in industry and in academia. She has advised the Government on a range of education and technology issues, led the HM Treasury King Review on sustainable transport and is on the Committee for Climate Change. In November 2009, she was appointed as a member of the group to conduct an independent review of Higher Education Funding and Student Finance.

Peter Lambert

Peter Lambert is Professor of Microbiology in the School of Life and Health Sciences at Aston University, Birmingham. His main research interests are in infections caused by bacteria, particularly how they can be treated with antibiotics and what can be done when bacteria become resistant to antibiotics. This has been of increasing concern over the past 10 years with the emergence of hospital acquired infections due to bacteria such as MRSA and Clostridium difficile. Broader interests concern the diversity of bacteria in the world and how microbes can be used in the service of mankind.

Peter Lane

Peter Lane is Professor of Clinical Immunology at the MRC Centre for Immune Regulation, the Institute for Biomedical Research at Birmingham Medical School. He works on the molecular and cellular basis of CD4 memory, as he believes that understanding these mechanisms will provide important new therapies for human diseases.

Veronica Lawrie

Veronica Lawrie is an Ecologist with Atkins, the global multi-disciplinary consultancy. Her work is to provide ecological input for a range of commercial and infrastructure projects in the UK. Her particular expertise includes botanical and protected species surveys, ecological impact assessment and mitigation plans.

Richard Lilford

Richard Lilford is Professor of Clinical Epidemiology and Head of the Division of Primary Care, Occupational and Public Health at the University of Birmingham. He is also Director of the Birmingham Clinical Research

Academy. Formerly a consultant in obstetrics and gynaecology, he was Head of Department of Obstetrics and Gynaecology at the University of Leeds. His research interests are the methodology of clinical trials, patient safety, statistics (including the application of Bayesian analyses to medical and health-related research) and in health economics.

Janet Lord

Janet Lord is Professor of Immune Cell Biology at the University of Birmingham. Her research focuses upon the effects of ageing upon the immune system and how this predisposes to age-related diseases such as Rheumatoid Arthritis. She also investigates how stress, both physical (hip fracture) and emotional (depression or bereavement), can further compound the age-related loss of immune function as humans age. More recently she has begun to investigate ways to improve immunity in older adults, for example through exercise.

Helen Maddock

Dr Helen Maddock is Principal Lecturer in Cardiovascular Physiology and Pharmacology at Coventry University, and is Editor of the *British Society for Cardiovascular Research Journal Bulletin*. She has worked for AstraZeneca and GlaxoSmithKline as well as undertaking research at UCL's Hatter Institute and Centre or Cardiology. Her current research includes investigating the role of reactive oxygen species, mitochondrial injury and apoptosis in myocardial stress, and also the development of novel therapies for the treatment of diseases related to the cardiovascular system.

Kathleen Maitland

Dr Kathleen Maitland is a lecturer in the Department of Computing, Telecommunications and Networks (CTN) at Birmingham City University. Her research interests are requirements engineering, information systems evolution, fuzzy logic and other non-classical logic systems, human–computer interaction and e-commerce.

Tim Mason

Professor Timothy Mason is Director of the Sonochemistry Centre at Coventry University. Having studied chemistry at Southampton University from 1964 to 1970, he spent two years at Amherst College USA before moving to Coventry University in 1975. He was awarded a DSc from Southampton for this research into sonochemistry in 1996. He is president of the European Society of Sonochemistry and is the editor in chief of the journal *Ultrasonics Sonochemistry*. His interests in sonochemistry cover environmental protection, materials processing, food processing, electrochemistry and therapeutic ultrasound.

Robin May

Robin May is based in the School of Biosciences at the University of Birmingham. His research focuses on the interaction between pathogens and their hosts and, in particular, on how infectious organisms evade the innate immune system.

Chris McCabe

Professor Chris McCabe holds a Chair in Endocrinology. His research focuses on mechanisms of thyroid, breast and colorectal tumourigenisis. In his spare time, he writes forensic thrillers as John Macken – *Dirty Little Lies* (2007), *Trial by Blood* (2008), *Breaking Point* (2009) and *Control* (2010) – having previously published five novels under the name John McCabe (*Stickleback, Paper, Snakeskin, Big Spender* and *Herding Cats*).

Roger McFadden

Roger McFadden is a senior lecturer in pharmacology in the Department of Nursing and Women's Health at Birmingham City University and is responsible for the delivery of post-graduate pharmacology at BCU. A member of the Association for Nurse Prescribing, he was part of the team that developed one of the first non-medical prescribing courses in the UK. His main area of research is in nurse education. He is the author of *Introducing Pharmacology for Nursing and Health Care*, published in July 2009 by Pearson.

Graham Medley

Professor Graham Medley works in the area of infectious disease epidemiology, and has over 120 refereed publications on the transmission dynamics and control of a diverse range of pathogens and hosts. His research work combines statistical and mathematical modelling to produce quantitative frameworks that can contribute to both understanding the biology and ecology of pathogens, as well as providing a basis for rational design of cost-effective control programmes. More recently, he has become interested in the economic, political and legal drivers of infectious disease control.

Paul Moss

Professor Paul Moss is Head of the School of Cancer Sciences at the University of Birmingham and Director of the Birmingham Cancer Research UK Centre. He is a clinical haematologist and has a major research interest in the role of the immune system in protection from cancer and viral infection.

Ian Nabney

Ian Nabney is Professor of Computer Science at Aston University. He is a member of the Neural Computing Research Group and his research is in pattern analysis. He specialises in developing applications with industrial and medical partners in such areas as data visualisation, energy price forecasting, and probabilistic models of risk in jet engine design. His software toolbox, Netlab, has over 35,000 users around the world.

Elizabeth Oliver-Jones

Elizabeth Oliver-Jones is Professor in the Department of Biological Sciences at Warwick University. Her research focus is around the study of early cell interactions in amphibians, about the little known molecular mechanisms by which vertebrate embryos achieve the myriad of complex patterns and cell types found in the adult animal. This work is of importance in understanding cell signalling, and in the relationships between genes and development.

the contributors

Michael Overduin

Michael Overduin, Professor of Structural Biology at the University of Birmingham, solves the structures of proteins involved in cancer and infection using magnets in the Henry Wellcome Building.

Mark Pallen

Mark Pallen is Professor of Microbial Genomics at the University of Birmingham, and author of *The Rough Guide to Evolution* (2009). He obtained his medical education at Cambridge and the London Hospital Medical College before completing his specialist training as a medical microbiologist at St Bartholomew's. In the mid-90s while completing a PhD in molecular bacteriology at Imperial College, he led a student team to victory in *University Challenge*. He held a chair in microbiology at Queen's University, Belfast before moving to Birmingham in 2001.

Andrew Peet

Dr Andrew Peet is a Clinical Research Fellow and Honorary Consultant Paediatric Oncologist at the University of Birmingham and the Oncology Department at Birmingham Children's Hospital. Initially trained in chemical physics at Cambridge and the University of California Berkeley, he studied medicine at St George's Hospital Medical School, London before training as a paediatrician in the West Midlands. His main research interests are developing and evaluating functional imaging for the non-invasive diagnosis, management and understanding of childhood brain tumours. The clinical research is linked to a lab programme investigating the underlying biological effects that give rise to the imaging findings including the effects of drugs.

Yvonne Perrie

Professor Yvonne Perrie is Chair in Drug Delivery in the School of Life Sciences at the University of Aston. She is also a qualified pharmacist. Her research is focused on the advancement and strategic development of drug delivery systems to facilitate effective delivery and targeting of drugs and vaccines. This research addresses key issues within the pharmaceutical field and, by developing and formulating such systems, aims to provide practical solutions and realistic options to enhance healthcare.

David Pink

Professor David Pink leads the Crop Improvement Group at Warwick HRI, University of Warwick carrying out a multidisciplinary crop improvement research on a range of vegetables (brassica, lettuce, carrot and onion) and narcissus. He has over 25 years experience in breeding research and his current interest is in the development of tools and resources to facilitate the improvement of economically important quantitative traits through the exploitation of natural variation found in older varieties and wild relatives of crops. His research is funded by Defra, BBSRC and industry. David is a member of the scientific advisory committee of the British Beet Research Organisation, the Defra Plant Varieties and Seeds Tribunal panel, the production sub group of the Defra Fruit and Vegetable Task Force, the Rural Affairs Committee of the BBC, the Defra Sustainable Arable LINK project management committee and is Scientific Adviser to the Field Vegetable Panel of the HDC and a member of the BBSRC pool of expert assessors.

Jon Preece

Jon Preece is Professor of Nanoscale Chemistry at the University of Birmingham. His research is focused on the interdisciplinary nature of nanoscale chemistry, including nanostructuring surfaces via the integration of top-down and bottom-up methodologies, gene delivery based on polycations, nanotribology, liquid crystals and nanoscale electronics.

Vinesh Raja

Professor Vinesh Raja is currently the interim director of the Institute of Digital Healthcare and head of the Informatics and Virtual Reality Group, International Digital Lab, Warwick Manufacturing Group, University of Warwick. His main research focus is on digital healthcare – innovative applications of ICT for healthcare improvements through business process reengineering and redesign of services. Projects includes: eHealth, Remote Patient Monitoring, innovative education for wellbeing, assistive technologies, virtual surgery and digital human anatomy.

Karim Raza

Dr Karim Raza is a Clinical Senior Lecturer and Honorary Consultant Rheumatologist. He qualified in medicine from Oxford University and currently works at the MRC Centre for Immune Regulation at the University of Birmingham. His main research interests are in the pathology of early inflammatory arthritis and the prediction of the development of rheumatoid arthritis in patients with early synovitis. (co-authors Chris Buckley and Andrew Filer)

Georgina Rippon

Professor Gina Rippon is Associate Dean of Postgraduate Taught Programmes and International Relations in the School of Life and Health Sciences, Aston University. Her research involves the application of brain imaging techniques, particularly electroencephalography (EEG) and Magnetoencephalography (MEG), to studies of normal and abnormal cognitive processes, most recently in the study of Autism Spectrum Disorders. She is currently associated with the development of two new research centres at Aston University, the Aston Brain Centre (ABC) and the Aston Research Centre for Healthy Ageing (ARCHA). She is also a past President of the British Association of Cognitive NeuroScience (previously British Psychophysiology Society) and a member of the Scientific Committee of the International Organisation of Psychophysiology.

Peter Sadler

Professor Peter Sadler is Head of Warwick's Chemistry Department. His research interests are the chemistry of metals in medicine (bioinorganic chemistry, inorganic chemical biology and medicine), and the design and chemical mechanism of action of therapeutic metal complexes, including organometallic arene anticancer complexes, photoactivated metal anticancer complexes (for photochemotherapy), metallomacrocycles as antivirals and stem-cell-mobilising agents, and metalloantibiotics. Besides synthesis of co-ordination complexes, his research involves studies of interactions with targets such as RNA, DNA and proteins, and often industrial and international interdisciplinary collaborations.

James Shippen

Dr James Shippen is a Chartered Mechanical Engineer with industrial experience in the medical, automotive, defence and aerospace industries. He is currently employed in the Industrial Design department at Coventry University where he researches mathematical modelling and stimulation of biomechanics and develops analysis code to solve biomechanical problems.

Stuart Slater

Stuart Slater is currently Director of the Institute of Gaming and Animation in the West Midlands. His active research in video games includes articles in leading magazines and journals and a range of consultancy in both games for education and emotionally responsive game characters. He currently also teaches games programming at the University of Wolverhampton where he has taught games programming to developers in several leading games companies.

Tony Smith

Tony Smith is Professor in Oral Biology at the School of Dentistry at the University of Birmingham. He is also Editor-in-Chief of the *Journal of Dental Research*. He leads an active research group on pulp biology and regeneration. He also has a long-term research programme focussed on cell behaviour in the dentine-pulp complex and is interested in the modulation of cell behaviour during tissue regeneration and engineering and in response to dental restorative procedures. (co-author Iain Chapple)

Neil Stewart

Neil Stewart is a Professor in the Psychology Department at Warwick University. He conducts research in perception, mathematical psychology, and relative-rank models of judgement and decision making. (co-authors Gordon Brown and Alex Wood)

Susannah Thorpe

Dr Susannah Thorpe is a lecturer in Animal Behaviour at the University of Birmingham. Her research has focused on the locomotion and ecology of the great apes (including humans) and, in particular, the evolution of human bipedalism. Her work has recently been published in *Science* and *Proceedings of the National Academy of Science* and she has presented at conferences worldwide.

Brian Tighe

Professor Brian Tighe is leader of Biomaterials Research at Aston University. His own research focuses on the design, synthesis and applications of biomedical polymers, a significant proportion of which are hydrogels, a term frequently used to describe polymers swollen with water. Current interests include novel materials for ophthalmic applications, drug delivery systems, bioadhesive polymers, synthetic materials for articular cartilage, lung surfactant and cornea. The research is interdisciplinary and involves strong interactive connections with relevant industrial companies.

Jim Tucker

Dr Jim Tucker studied for his BSc and PhD in Chemistry at Kings College, London. After post-doc work in Japan and France, he was Lecturer in Inorganic Chemistry at Exeter before moving in 2005 to his present position at Birmingham University where he is Reader in Supramolecular Chemistry, and currently holds an EPSRC Leadership Fellowship.

Ann Vernallis

Dr Ann Vernallis is a Lecturer in the School of Life and Health Sciences at the University of Aston. She is interested in cell signalling. As a post-doctoral fellow, she studied cytokine receptor interactions in the IL-6 family. At Aston, she has studied the secretion of Leukemia Inhibitory Factor (LIF), the pro-inflammatory activities of lipoteichoic acid from Gram-positive bacteria and cytokine levels in patients with infections. She is currently working on the anti-inflammatory effects of tetracyclines, and she collaborates on studies of neuron/astrocyte interactions in a neuronal stem cell model.

Elizabeth Wellington

Professor Liz Welington is an environmental microbiologist, and has been involved in ecological research and soil microbiology for over 20 years. With a personal Chair, she is part of the Microbiology section within the Department of Biological Sciences at Warwick University, and was co-director of the Warwick Systems Biology Centre (2005–07) to co-ordinate interdisciplinary research allowing biological systems to be modelled. Her current research focuses on the fate of bacterial pathogens in the environment and understanding the functional properties of soil bacteria.

Michael West

Professor Michael West is Dean at Aston Business School. He has authored, edited or co-edited 16 books and published over 150 articles for scientific and practitioner publications as well as chapters in scholarly books. He is a Fellow of the British Psychological Society, the American Psychological Association, the International Association of Applied Psychologists, is a Chartered Fellow of the Chartered Institute of Personal and Development. His areas of research interest are team and organisational innovation and effectiveness, particularly in relation to the organisation of health services. He lectures widely both nationally and internationally about the results of his research and his ideas for developing effective and innovative healthcare organisations.

Adrian Williams

Adrian Williams has been the Professor of Clinical Neurology, Queen Elizabeth Hospital and University of Birmingham since 1989. Previously he trained at Cambridge, National Hospital for Nervous Diseases, London and NIH Bethesda. He first described MPTP poisoning causing Parkinsonism in 1979 and is interested in xenobiotic biochemistry in particular the nicotinamide methylation path and more generally in the evolutionary origins of disease. He has recently rediscovered descriptions of Pellagra and its many manifestations including premature ageing and Parkinsonism and reinterpreted some aspects of its pathogenesis such as the excess infection rate with NADH supplying symbionts.

James Wolffsohn

Professor James Wolffsohn studied Ophthalmic and Physiological Optics at UMIST, Manchester, achieving a first class degree. He qualified to practice optometry independently following a pre-registration year Moorfield's Eye Hospital, London. Following this, he completed a PhD on at Cardiff University. He commenced a clinical / research position at the Victorian College of Optometry, University of Melbourne in 1997. In 2000, he returned to the UK and a position at Aston University, where he was Head of Optometry from 2004 to 2009, being awarded a personal Chair in 2007. He is now Deputy Executive Dean for the School of Life and Health Sciences. His research and teaching interests mainly revolve around intraocular lenses, contact lenses, low vision and the measurement of accommodation, having published over 90 peer-reviewed academic papers and given numerous international presentations. He is also a past President of the British Contact Lens Association. He has recently published the *Low Vision Manual* with Professor Jonathan Jackson and an Eye Essentials Series book *Imaging*.

Alex Wood

Alex Wood is Lecturer in the School of Psychological Sciences at the University of Manchester. His research interests cover all areas of personality, particularly how personality influences well-being. His current focus is on gratitude, authenticity and well-being. He and Gordon are working on a relative model of personality and social decision-making. (co-authors Gordon Brown and Neil Stewart)

Introduction

Keith Richards

In a recent edition of *Times Higher Education*, Jorge Cham included the following in a tongue-in-cheek guide to 'deciphering academese':

'Results were found through direct experimentation'	=	'The data agreed quite well with the predicted model.'
'We played around with it until it worked'	=	'If you turn the page upside down and squint, it doesn't look too different.'

Humour, though, is sometimes rendered poignant by force of circumstances: a false claim in an IPCC report on climate change and a few hacked emails from climate scientists at the University of East Anglia have stripped these light-hearted observations of their innocence. When Spin meets Science nothing is to be trusted.

It seems an odd time, then, to be introducing a book on science and optimism – better to hunker down well below the parapet. But there are shifts in mood, attitude and policy that are drawing science into new alignments that may have profound consequences for all of us, and in the public arena the sound of something different and altogether more worrying: a disturbing categorisation of science and religion as alternative belief systems. This first surfaced in the protests of creationists but is currently most strident in the climate debate, where words like *religion*, *agnostic* and *believer* are bandied about. If we are not to be misled by such talk, there has never been a more important time to listen to the voice of science and the ideal that it represents.

As the contributions in this collection demonstrate, scientists have different views about issues related to global warming, as they have different views of most things. But what they all agree on, what they are committed to, is *doing science*. For them, it's not a question of whether or not they happen to believe in their findings – it's whether they got the science right.

That's not how most people see science. Science, as any daily newspaper will tell you, is about discoveries, facts, finding the truth and changing the world. For professional scientists, living down the wilful distortions and extravagant promises made on their behalf by the popular press is an occupational necessity, but seeing science downgraded to just another belief system is harder to swallow. Scientists, like the rest of us, have plenty of beliefs, but the pursuit of science does not allow the luxury of indulging them at the expense of proper procedure.

Science is a way of trying to understand and explain the way things work. It is driven by endless curiosity coupled with a determination not to be beguiled by easy answers. Two examples will illustrate what this means, the first an embarrassing admission of my own failure to live up to these ideals in the preparation of this collection. When editing Mark Pallen's paper, I came across his quotation from the Gerald Manley Hopkins poem, 'Pied Beauty', referring to a 'brinded cow'. I thought this was a typo because I remembered it as 'brindled cow', so I decided to check.

On a good day you might call me a social scientist (at least the Faculty has yet to disown me), but this wasn't a good day, so instead of looking for falsification as any decent scientist would, I took the self-indulgent route and opted for verification. Into Google went 'brindled cow Hopkins', and because I looked for it I found it: out came pages and pages of confirmation, headed by a Wikipedia entry. I edited the text accordingly and moved on.

This is the sort of mistake that has been described as a Type 1 error, a false positive. Sloppy procedure. Mark was quickly back to me, gently pointing out that the original uses 'brinded'. Back in the Wikipedia entry I find my original quote, 'For skies of couple color as a brindled cow' and notice for the first time the spelling of 'color'. Then, taking the trouble to read on, I discover the following just five lines further down: 'he compares "skies of couple-colour" to a "brinded cow"'. Having first given my toes time to uncurl, I check this in an Oxford edition, make the necessary change, apologise and move on. No harm done – but then I'm not squaring up to the challenges of cancer or ageing.

My second example is simpler and infinitely more inspiring. In his entertaining contribution, David Jones explains how his work on muscle fatigue followed a particular line of enquiry for 30 years, but 'always with a slight nagging doubt'. Then a series of experiments revealed to him that he and his colleagues had been fundamentally wrong for all that time. Writing off 30 years of work would plunge most mortals into deep denial or drive them into the arms of a convenient therapist, but David is a scientist – he became very excited!

Science does funny things to people. It fills them with an insatiable desire to understand while denying them easy answers, it tempts them with the infinite possibilities while shackling them with unbending rules of procedure – and it denies them rest. Discovery in science is never the end, always a beginning, a new set of questions and possibilities. That's why David was excited and why the treasures in this collection are to be found not just in the wonderful discoveries and insights these scientists share with us but in the prospects they open up. This is optimism with a purpose.

Of course, the richness of such a collection offers both delight and illumination in itself, as is evident from the following questions:
- What's the connection between lobsters and leukaemia?
- Which child's toy was used in the development of the first contact lens?
- How many litres of water does it take to produce (a) a litre of milk and (b) a kilogram of beef? (Add a nought to each of the figures you've just come up with.)
- How many people have become infected with TB in the last minute?
- If you wanted to avoid injury would you choose to be a racing driver, a footballer, a ballet dancer or a builder?

- Which country was primarily responsible for the eradication of smallpox?

The answers to all of these are to be found in the contributions that follow, but even more interesting are the questions waiting to be answered. Derek Alderson tells us in his contribution that over the last 40 years the incidence of oesophageal adenocarcinoma has risen from just one-tenth to three-quarters of all oesophageal cancers in the UK and that the UK has the highest incidence of this form of cancer in the world, but as yet we don't know why. The writers in this collection convey the excitement, and sometimes the urgency, of confronting questions such as these. Theirs is an optimism grounded in engagements of this kind – and it is all the more inspiring for that.

Contributors, whose work embraces both natural and social sciences, were asked to draw on their own research in responding to a very simple question previously posed by John Brockman: *What are you optimistic about?* The result is a rich and varied collection which gives voice to a range of views and opinions in a variety of styles.

The organisation of such diverse material must inevitably be a personal matter, but we wished to take the reader on a journey in four stages, beginning in familiar surroundings looking in on the work of scientists, then moving gradually towards their world until finally we are inside looking out. We therefore divided the collection into four parts, each comprising chapters related to the same broad theme, and within each chapter we gathered the contributions themselves:

Part 1:   The Microcosm: Tackling the big challenges

Cancer and *Changing bodies*

Part 2:   The Macrocosm: Interacting with our world

Living in the natural world and *Living in the virtual world*

Part 3:   Transformations

Getting to the heart of things and *Changing behaviour*

Part 4:   The ways of science

Working together, Thinking differently and *From where I stand*

Part 1: *The Microcosm: Tackling the big challenges* begins with the human body, the microcosm, and a challenge that all of us will recognise: the treatment of cancer. The first two contributions, by **Moss** and **James**, provide succinct overviews of how and where the battles are being fought, as well as offering insights into the shape of future work, while the excitement of current research into two types of cancer is conveyed by **Alderson** and **Peet**. This is of course part of a much bigger war being fought on many fronts and marshalling different resources, as the contributions from **Johnson**, **Craddock**, **Conway** and **Lilford** show.

The body itself is the focus of the second chapter and in taking ageing as her subject **Griffiths** highlights something that presents particular challenges. The chapter, though, is more wide-ranging, holding out hope of life-transforming developments in the fields of rheumatoid arthritis (**Buckley et al**), eyesight (**Wolffsohn**), oral and dental disease (**Chapple and Smith**), and membrane proteins (**Bill**). The more successful we are in addressing these issues, the more pressing becomes the issue of ageing itself, and the last three papers in the chapter address this in very different ways. While **Lord** shows how even simple changes have significant effects on ageing, **Williams** proposes a radical response that dares to raise the prospect of immortality and **Rippon** shows how running repairs might be made to the brain itself.

Individual survival, though, will depend ultimately on the fate of our species as a whole and for this we are dependent on the macrocosm, the environment within which we live.

Part 2: *Macrocosm: Interacting with our world* begins in the natural world and the first three contributions, by **Bugg**, **Bridgwater** and **Hornung**, respond to the energy challenge currently facing us by exploring the potential of bio-ethanol, biomass and biochar. Issues in transport and food are addressed by papers in which **King** assesses the potential of electric drive vehicles and **Coates** shows how plant evolution may hold the key to a new generation of food resources. The more immediate environment, for city dwellers at least, is explored by the final three contributions in the opening chapter. The papers by **Bastin** and **Lawrie** are complementary, the former demonstrating the potential of raising consciousness and the latter focusing on the way partnership can work to develop urban reserves, while

Charlesworth adds a further dimension by proposing a simple but radical transformation of the urban scene.

How much of our future will be spent in the physical world and how much in the virtual is a question the collection does not address, but it does open up some interesting prospects on how the latter might develop. The opening contributions of *Chapter 4* explore ways in which computers are already transforming the nature of our experience, in terms of how they facilitate the achievement of personal goals (**Beale**) and promote personal development (**Slater**). More specific aspects of the human–computer interface are explored by **Homer**, revealing how near-field communications can unlock the potential of the mobile phone, **Foss** in his stimulating but disturbing revelations about quantum information, and **Raja** in an exciting description of full-body motion control. These prospects extend our current experiences, but **Maitland** and **Burden** take us into a world in which the interface between humans and computers has evolved to the point where current distinctions are more difficult to sustain.

Tackling the problems and challenges that threaten our survival and well-being engages science in profound issues of what we are and how the world we inhabit is constituted. Its response to these issues has the potential to transform our understanding or behaviour, reconfiguring our relationship with our environment.

Part 3: *Transformations* explores this potential from two different perspectives. *Chapter 5* reveals how science is tackling fundamental questions and highlights some of the implications of this. The huge potential of monoclonal antibody therapy, **McFadden** argues, may provide the 'magic bullet' that will enable us to tackle currently intractable diseases, while **Pallen** shows the powerful knowledge that genome sequencing places at our disposal in this struggle. One outcome of success here could be population growth, but if **Pink** is right developments in crop science may offer a solution to this problem, while contributions from **Frampton**, **Lane** and **Overduin** all reflect exciting developments in our understanding of the cell as a key to unlocking fundamental mysteries. The chapter concludes with a consideration of how such research might transform the way we see the world (**May**) and the way we respond to global health challenges (**Perrie**).

Chapter 6 sees a shift in viewpoint, directing attention to the nature of behaviour. It begins with **Barrett**'s sobering picture highlighting the fundamental importance of behaviour change in the fight against HIV/AIDS – and the challenge this represents. **Brown et al** and **French** address behaviour change directly, showing the impact it can have on our sense of well-being and general health, while **Calvert** and **Chappell** focus on the potential of work on understanding the brain. The last three papers in the chapter explore the relationship between science and society, beginning with **Green**'s discussion of how incentives work and the implications of this at a global level. **Chandler**'s subject is the relationship between science and society and the need for scientists to engage with basic values, while **Grant** touches on its power to influence these values in his demonstration of how research can impact on the delivery of justice.

Stereotypical views of scientists reinforce deeper misconceptions about the discipline of science and those who live by its precepts, one of which is that scientists are isolated individuals, interacting with their fellows only by necessity. If this is so, we have a deviant sample here, for a recurring theme in this collection is the idea of connection, of systems, of collaboration – an understanding that doing science involves a responsibility towards a larger community of inquirers.

Part 4: *The ways of science* takes up this theme. *Chapter 7* begins with different perspectives on the relationship between blue skies research and its application, a key debate as funding becomes increasingly influenced by considerations of demonstrable impact. **Maddock** sets the scene by showing the potential of translational research, a theme taken up by **Kelly** in her illustration of how collaboration can contribute to work on liver disease. The case for blue skies research is passionately presented by **Oliver-Jones** and developed by **Anderson** but with a twist highlighting the sociability of scientists. **Vernallis** uses cytokines as an example of the interplay of basic and clinical sciences and **Tucker** widens the scope of collaboration even further to embrace interdisciplinarity. **Green** and **Preece** demonstrate in different ways their commitment to collaboration, while **Wellington** draws attention to the need to train and encourage a new breed of young scientists with wide-ranging expertise. The chapter ends with a taste of the directions this new research might take, beginning with **Franklyn**'s case for evidence-based medicine and moving on to papers by

Gifford and **Nabney** highlighting the potential contributions of systems biology and probability theory.

Our view of science tends to be compartmentalised and the aim of *Chapter 8* is to challenge this by illustrating the interconnectivity of scientific research. It begins with engineering, which perhaps more than anything else conjours up stereotypical images. It might surprise some readers, then, to discover the vital role it plays in joint replacement (**Hukins**), prolonging the working lives of ballet dancers (**Shippen**) and understanding our daily soundworld (**Cain**). The next two contributions return to the world of health, **Jackson** highlighting the importance of occupational health and **Medley** offering an insight into collaborative efforts to understand the spread of infectious diseases. The papers by **Sadler** and **Lambert** take us back to the unexpected, the former showing how an understanding of inorganic elements can offer a new way of tackling disease and the latter introducing the incredible world of microbiology. **Thorpe** and **Cohen** address issues in evolution, the first from the unexpected perspective of orangutan locomotion, and the chapter concludes on a positive note with **West**'s case for staying connected.

The collection ends with view from the scientists' world, a glimpse of the way scientists see their work. At the heart of **Tighe**'s contribution is the inspiring and in many ways astounding story of how contact lenses were invented, a testament to the persistence and invention of scientists, while **Jones**' story demonstrates how openness to error may be the foundation of success. **Hilton** and **Berry** place such success within the wider perspectives of public engagement and motivating a new generation, drawing attention to the wider responsibilities of scientists. The voice of that new generation can be heard in **Edwards**' reflections on her work, and juxtaposed with these is **Mason**'s retrospective on a long and successful career. We finish in the company of **McCabe**, inside his air-conditioned laboratory looking out on a struggle between weeds and bureaucracy as the year moves from winter towards summer. And in this connection between the personal and the universal we touch on something at the heart of the collection, a sense of playing a part in a much bigger story.

On the 350th anniversary of the founding of the Royal Society, science in this country may be at a watershed as scientific research faces funding cuts and realignments that will affect our future in ways we cannot predict. The contributions to this collection demonstrate incontrovertibly the huge potential of science in this region and this country – and the realisation of that potential depends on the availability of adequate funding. If we can add our voices to those of scientists, we might just make a difference in the debates to come.

On the rim of a two pound coin, you will find the words of a former Warden of the Royal Mint: 'Standing on the shoulders of giants.' The warden, Isaac Newton, was echoing words that can be traced back to Bernard of Chartres hundreds of years earlier, but from his mouth the observation has particular resonance, issuing from what was arguably the dawn of science as we know it today. Like Newton, the contributors to this collection are able to see further by virtue of the tradition in which they work, and if we take the trouble to listen to them carefully and support their work, we thereby express our gratitude to the generations of researchers who have lived within science's uncompromising orbit – knowing that the dark spaces beyond are inimical to our survival.

PART I

The Microcosm – Tackling the big challenges

CHAPTER 1
Cancer

Cancer – controlled within one generation?

Paul Moss

'Cancer will be controlled within one generation.'

t first sight this statement might appear wildly optimistic, perhaps even controversial. How can we make such a claim at a time when we might be diagnosed at any day with an incurable malignant disease? Many cancers, such as those of the pancreas, lung, oesophagus or brain, have limited treatment options and most patients will succumb to their disease. However, my feeling is that progress in the fight against cancer is so relentless and inexorable that this claim can indeed be justified.

What is cancer? Ever since multi-cellular organisms evolved from single-celled life forms over 500 million years ago, they have had to contend with the possibility that just one of their cells might start to divide uncontrollably and threaten the life of the organism. This complication is cancer and, as might be expected, our bodies have developed powerful mechanisms to prevent and limit this potentially devastating event. Indeed, the body's ability to prevent cancer is impressive. Each of us contains around 100 trillion cells and these divide many thousands of times during our lifetime. Despite these impressive numbers, perhaps only one-third to one-half of us will develop cancer during our lifetime.

Nevertheless, perhaps largely due to environmental factors and the way we live our lives today, cancer is a huge clinical problem for the global population at the current time.

Research into cancer has a long and proud history. The first important observations were 'epidemiological', which relates to the fact that they were observed the pattern of cancer cases in society. In the eighteenth century, Bernado Ramazzini noticed that breast cancer was particularly common in Italian nuns and we now know that this is because pregnancy is highly protective against the development of this disease. In 1775, the famous British surgeon Percival Pott identified the link between boy chimney sweeps and the development of cancer of the scrotum. This important observation led to the banning of this practice within the UK. However, as well as improvements in epidemiology, striking developments have been seen the last 100 years in our understanding of both how cancer develops within a cell and the range of treatments that can be offered.

Advances in our understanding of cancer cell biology have followed the breathtaking progress in general biological research over the last 150 years. These include the observation that organisms are made up of individual cells and the finding in the 1940s that DNA was the hereditary material that passed genetic information from one generation to the next. In 1980, Fred Sanger won the Nobel Prize for developing a procedure that allowed us to sequence DNA for the first time and therefore 'read' the genetic code. I remember being a medical student when, in 1983, the first report of a mutation in a cellular gene was observed in a cancer cell. This led to the concept that cancer was due to acquired mutations in our DNA which leads that cell to undergo uncontrolled division. Due to the fact that this mutation is in DNA, it is passed from generation to generation and every cancer cell acquires this damage. Importantly, as cancers develop they acquire more and more damaging mutations to their DNA and thus acquire new properties, such as the ability to spread throughout the body.

This work has been greatly extended and we now know many hundreds of cancer genes, many of which have been directly investigated as new therapeutic targets. Last year, a remarkable experiment was performed in which the DNA of a cancer cell was completely sequenced and then compared with the normal DNA sequence of the person from which the cancer was derived. Considering that the complete sequence is 3,000 million base pairs in both cases, you can see the extraordinary amount of technological work that this involved. In the future it is almost certainly the case that when patients are diagnosed with a cancer, their cancer genome will be completely sequenced so that we can understand the personal nature of their disease and use appropriate therapy.

Dramatic changes are also taking place in the way we treat cancer. Almost immediately after the discovery of X-rays in 1895 they were used as a form of radiotherapy for cancer, which perhaps shows our compelling desire to try new therapies in the treatment of cancer. The first attempts at chemotherapy were performed in the 1940s when single drugs were used in children suffering from acute leukaemia. These were not successful in curing patients but did provide temporary relief, and provided an important clue as to the way that treatment needed to be developed. In the 1960s, doctors started to use combinations of drugs and managed to begin to cure some patients with leukaemia. When this was extended in the 1970s, we were able to bring about long-term cures in patients with a variety of diseases, such as lymphoma and testicular cancer, and this approach to chemotherapy has now been applied to many types of tumours.

Other treatments have continued to progress. Surgery still plays an important role in the cure of many cancers, and surgical oncology procedures have improved dramatically over this time. The use of antibodies, which are derived from natural white cells in our body which fight cancer and infections, has been introduced into treatment of many cancers and the use of these agents for the treatment of lymphoma has led to the biggest increase in survival that we have seen with any single drug. However, perhaps the most optimistic development over the last 20 years has been the introduction of new types of drugs which block pathways within cancer cells, which are critical in allowing cancer cells to divide. These drugs are called 'signal transduction inhibitors' and target specific DNA mutations within cancer cells. The first such drug is imatinib, used to treat chronic myeloid leukaemia, which is now bringing about long-term remissions in patients with just a single daily tablet. We do not yet know whether this represents a 'cure' for this disease but things are looking increasingly optimistic.

Despite the bleak outlook for many cancers, we are making steady progress in many areas of cancer therapy. Breast cancer survival is now markedly improved due to a combination of treatment with chemotherapy, radiotherapy and hormone blocking drugs, and 85% of patients with Hodgkin's lymphoma can expect to be cured.

As a population, we constantly hear in the media about new 'cancer hopes', yet as these often take time to be translated into clinical benefit it is easy to get despondent and disillusioned about the rate of progress.

However, as we look at what we have achieved over the last 30 years it is truly phenomenal and I am extremely confident that even greater progress can be made within the next comparable time. The translation into new therapies of our remarkable knowledge of how a cancer cell develops will surely lead to substantial improvements in how we control this devastating disease. This will take time and money. We have a remarkable group of strong cancer charities within the UK and the support of the British public in this fight has been phenomenal.

When I lecture my medical students today, I challenge them to think that they can be the first generation to be largely free of the fear of cancer. This is a sobering thought but can certainly be achieved.

Targeted therapies — a new generation

Nicholas James

I have been fascinated by the treatment of cancer and the underlying science since early on in medical school. The first clinical attachment I carried out was on the leukaemia wards at Bart's, where I subsequently also worked as a junior doctor. The striking and very exciting thing about the treatment of leukaemia at that time was that patients presented with very advanced illness which a generation earlier would have rapidly been fatal. For many of these patients by the 1980s there was a very real prospect of long-term cure, albeit with relatively toxic treatment.

Once I had completed my medical training I took the decision to specialise in the treatment of cancer, choosing ultimately to specialise in tumours of the kidney, bladder and prostate. When I commenced my training the treatment of advanced prostate cancer was essentially confined to hormone manipulations dating back to the 1940s. Bladder cancer was known to respond to chemotherapy, but this treatment had not really changed for some time. The treatment of kidney cancer was particularly limited and was purely palliative once an attempt at curative surgery had failed.

The first half of my professional career to date was dominated by the introduction of new chemotherapy drugs. For bladder cancer, the advances were relatively modest, with only one drug of any real value appearing. In prostate cancer, however, a whole range of new drugs has now been developed, including new hormone therapies, chemotherapy, radioisotopes and bone-protecting agents. In addition, the use of existing therapies earlier in the disease process has improved survival rates substantially.

Kidney cancer best illustrates the likely future trends in cancer treatment. The study of a rare inherited form of kidney cancer called von Hippel-Lindau syndrome revealed one of the key abnormalities to be in a gene called VHL, after the inherited disease. Subsequent studies of the much commoner, non-inherited form of kidney cancer showed this VHL gene also to be damaged in a high proportion of cases. This allowed the development of drugs specifically targeting abnormalities present in the cancer cell but not present in normal cells. The resulting treatments were licensed initially in 2006 and have transformed the treatment options for kidney cancer.

This targeted molecular approach to cancer treatment also brings with it much more manageable treatment that can be readily administered to elderly patients with little in the way of serious side effects. This contrasts markedly with the sort of chemotherapy which I observed on the leukaemia wards early on in my career, which essentially could not be delivered to elderly patients in full dosage as it was simply too toxic. Even in areas such as the hormone therapy of prostate cancer which dates from the 1940s, we are now seeing the development of new targeted molecular treatments which focus upon the mechanisms whereby cancers escape from hormone control. Again, these treatments have very little in the way of serious toxicity and bring with them a prospect of further substantial advances in prognosis for patients with advanced prostate cancer.

The major fly in the ointment of these new drugs is the sheer cost of developing them. The global market for cancer drugs is around $30 billion at present and each year pharmaceutical industry and research charities spend between \$6 and \$8 billion on developing new drugs. Clearly this development must be paid for and this is reflected in the very high price of new drugs. The ability to pay for these drugs is proving challenging even to the most wealthy economies in the world and has been a major bone of contention, particularly in the UK where the threshold for paying for new treatments is rather lower than in other major Western economies. None the less, these funding problems are generic and not specific to the UK.

In the long run I am optimistic. First, that these new treatments will prove to be of great benefit to large numbers of cancer patients with a whole range of conditions worldwide. Secondly, the manufacturing costs for these new treatments are relatively modest, so as the new generation of targeted therapies come off patent they will doubtless become available very widely and very cheaply, albeit not for some years. Thirdly, I may be misguidedly optimistic that some way will be found to moderate the very high prices of new drugs either by accelerating the development process or through novel clinical trial methodologies, with consequent reduction in costs. This in turn would make these treatments available to more patients across the world.

The current wave of new cancer therapies reflects the dividend from decades of investment in understanding the molecular biology of the human being and cancer in particular. As a clinician I am now seeing this translating into a substantial improvement in treatment outcomes for patients, some of whom had previously very few treatment options. I have also seen improvements in patients with much commoner diseases such as prostate cancer where treatment options had really been static for some years.

Oesophageal cancer – targeting treatment

Derek Alderson

very year nearly 8,000 people in the UK are diagnosed with oesophageal (gullet) cancer. It is the fifth most common cause of cancer death in this country. A highly unusual feature of this aggressive tumour has been the change in its incidence in the last 30 years – the number of patients affected has doubled in that time. No other cancer in the West has behaved like this.

In parallel with this rise has been the emergence of adenocarcinoma as the most common type of oesophageal cancer, so that three-quarters of all oesophageal cancers in the UK are now of this histological sub-type compared with only 10% 40 years ago. In fact, the UK has the highest incidence of oesophageal adenocarcinoma in the world.

We have learned much about this particular type of cancer in recent years. It is five times more common in men than women, occurs generally at a younger age than many other common cancers and is strongly linked to chronic heartburn and being overweight. In some patients there is a recognisable pre-cancerous condition called Barrett's oesophagus that we now know is an adaptive response in the lining of the oesophagus to the reflux of gastric contents.

For every patient with Barrett's oesophagus, between 0.5 and 1% will develop an oesophageal adenocarcinoma within 12 months. The problem, however, is identifying the people who have this condition. Most people with heartburn (the usual cause is reflux of gastric contents into the lower gullet) do not have Barrett's oesophagus; those who do have it do not all complain of heartburn as the Barrett's lining is protective. Finding the Barrett's population is not easy.

Most patients therefore make their first presentation with a symptomatic cancer, usually with progressive difficulty swallowing food (dysphagia). Management of these patients is difficult. In the first instance the symptoms are distressing and weight loss is common.

Adenocarcinoma is a highly aggressive malignancy that spreads by local invasion to other vital structures in the chest, through lymph channels to lymph glands in the chest and abdomen and through the bloodstream to distant organs (usually the liver or lungs).

Identifying the exact extent of spread (cancer staging) is important because any of these types of spread can render the patient unsuitable for a treatment aimed at cure. In addition, curative treatment often involves a combination of chemotherapy and surgery, with a 5% risk that the patient will not survive the treatment. At the end of the day, of those patients who come through all of the staging, chemotherapy and surgery, only one-third are cured. Against this background, it is perhaps difficult to see what there is to be optimistic about!

Fortunately, there now seem genuine prospects of identifying patients at a pre-cancerous stage or at the earliest stages of disease. This 'molecular biology' allows the scientist and clinician not only to understand some of the basic mechanisms in cancer development, but also in the context of oesophageal cancer to identify patients 'at-risk' of developing this tumour, predicting the stage of disease, tailoring specific drug therapies to individual patients' tumours and identifying risks in relation to surgery. This work involves the linked disciplines of genomics (the study of the genes involved), proteomics (the study of the proteins made by these genes) and metabolomics (the study of the small molecules created by the cell at a specific point in time). Some researchers even consider metabolomics as a chemical fingerprint of cellular function.

Already genomics has allowed us to identify families of genes present in oesophageal adenocarcinomas that are particularly threatening. New therapies are already available in clinical trials in the UK to see how novel drugs can interfere with the function of these genes. The effects of these compounds in other cancers, notably breast, have revolutionised cancer management. As a result, many new compounds are likely to reach trials in humans in the next ten years.

The clinical impact of the newer technologies of proteomics and metabolomics remains largely unknown, but potentially could far outstrip the impact of genomics. The idea of identifying the one patient in 100 with Barrett's oesophagus destined to develop a cancer within 12 months on the basis of the production of a family of proteins or a metabolic fingerprint seemed fanciful a decade ago and yet now seems likely.

The 'holy grail' for the medical oncologist has been the ability to identify the patient who will respond to a specific therapy with a high degree of certainty, and thanks to approaches based on proteomics and metabolomics we are now within reach of this. No longer will we have to face the prospect of giving the patient only the side-effects of treatment without therapeutic benefit.

Where does this leave the surgeon in the future? At one end of the scale must be the management of those patients with the earliest stages of disease, where endoscopic treatments are appropriate to eliminate the trauma of major surgery and preserve function. The imaging technologies to allow us to recognise these lesions are already available, as are the tools for treatment. This means that surgery alone will be appropriate for those patients whose tumours are confined to the primary site, but without spread.

And if these are to be the surgical patients of the future, it behoves the surgeon to ensure that the surgical insult is minimised whilst not compromising the chances of cure.

Undoubtedly, in the fullness of time, the general trend must be away from the major surgery largely performed nowadays. Nevertheless, whilst it is reasonable to expect that better identification of the patient who will genuinely benefit from having oesophagectomy is likely to reduce the numbers of patients undergoing surgery, this may be offset by new chemotherapies offering potentially curative treatments to patients previously considered incurable.

Better identification of the patient who will genuinely benefit from having oesophagectomy is likely to reduce the numbers of patients undergoing surgery, but this may be offset by new chemotherapies offering potentially curative treatments to patients previously considered incurable. The identification of patients who are likely to benefit from the addition of surgery after such chemotherapy is again likely to be solved by the molecular biologist, but the use of minimal access (keyhole) surgery for oesophageal cancer is in its infancy. Training a generation of surgeons to apply this type of surgery responsibly and logically to our future patients will be a challenge in all Western countries – and one that the surgical community must rise to.

I am confident that oesophageal surgeons in the UK will meet this challenge; that an increasing proportion of patients will be treated by keyhole rather than open surgery; that the chances of success will be higher; and that outcomes in general for patients with oesophageal cancer will improve.

Brain tumour imaging – the dawn of a new era

Andrew Peet

remember very well a particular scene from the television series *Star Trek* which I saw when I was a child. The ship's doctor was attending to an unconscious crew member. He passed a small hand-held device over the patient's head and declared that he had a brain haemorrhage; a quick flick of a switch on the device, another pass of the device over the head and all was repaired. The patient awoke and was immediately back to normal. The creation of such a device certainly seemed very optimistic at the time! Could it ever become a reality?

I am an academic paediatric oncologist, dividing my time between looking after children with brain tumours and performing research into the development of new scanning techniques for their diagnosis and management. The quality of the images which we can now obtain of the inside of the head would be beyond the belief of the doctors who looked after children with brain tumours 50 years ago, when there were no useful imaging techniques and they had to rely on their clinical judgement and plain X-rays of the skull.

A major breakthrough came with the advent of CT scans, or CAT scans as the early ones were known. These allowed the first images of the inside of the head to be obtained and are still commonly used to detect brain tumours. However, these scans were rapidly superseded by magnetic resonance images (MRI), which give unparalleled views of the brain with resolution on a millimetre scale. These scans are now the gold standard for detection of most brain tumours.

Key advances have clearly been made in the imaging of brain tumours, but new techniques are being developed and evaluated which signal the dawn of a new era in brain tumour imaging. Attention is moving away from obtaining pictures of the inside of the head and towards understanding the nature of what is being seen. For, although conventional MRI is usually able to identify that a tumour is present, it does not tell us what type of tumour it is, whether the tumour will act aggressively or whether it will respond to treatment. Answering these questions is the goal of a new and flourishing field of scientific endeavour called functional imaging. Many of the techniques being developed can be performed on the same scanner as the conventional MRI scans, allowing them to be incorporated rapidly into clinical practice and leading to a minimum of inconvenience for the patient.

Perhaps the most widely investigated technique is magnetic resonance spectroscopy, which provides a biochemical profile of the tumour. These biochemical profiles have been found to be highly characteristic for certain tumours, making this a useful diagnostic tool. Impressive results have been shown by researchers at centres of expertise using the technique and the challenge has switched to translating these advances into routine clinical practice. Two recent projects for which I was the clinical manger, eTumour and Health Agents, have demonstrated that this can indeed be done across a number of centres with expertise in the EU. Now we need to show that the methods can be used in hospitals which do not have expertise in using these scans.

Although non-invasive diagnosis is an important goal for functional imaging, of more importance to oncologists such as myself is that some of the chemicals detected by magnetic resonance spectroscopy have been shown to be linked to tumour behaviour. Tumours with high levels of phosphocholine, lipids and glycine, for example, tend to behave very aggressively, whereas those with high myoinosital tend to behave more indolently. Such findings give the potential for these chemicals to be used to aid treatment decisions and for monitoring the success of treatment. Obviously, it is important to evaluate these biomarkers in clinical practice and this is a major aim of a programme of research in the UK which we lead from the University of Birmingham, funded by Cancer Research UK and the Engineering and Physical Sciences Research Council.

Magnetic resonance spectroscopy is only one of a number of complementary functional imaging techniques. Diffusion weighted imaging can determine the cellular density of the tumour, which is also related to tumour aggressiveness and is reduced when the tumour responds to treatment. The technique can also be used to image nerve tracts in the brain to determine whether these have been invaded by the tumour, aiding diagnosis and surgical approach. Perfusion imaging is used to measure the blood supply to the tumour and this has become particularly important since many of the new anti-cancer drugs being developed target tumour blood vessels.

Identifying potential therapeutic targets within the tumour is currently a major strategy for cancer management, and functional imaging is set to play an important role in this approach. Where key molecular targets are identified then these can be imaged directly, an approach called molecular imaging, which can be based on magnetic resonance imaging or on a different scanning modality called positron emission tomography (PET). Clearly, one of the major challenges is to learn how to use all these complementary functional imaging techniques to obtain the most important information for clinical decision-making, and this is another major aim of our programme of research in the UK and beyond.

So, if new imaging methods can tell us so much about problems within the brain, can they also be used to treat patients? Well actually there is a long history of this. X-rays that are used for CT scans, at higher doses, are used as the basis for radiotherapy, the main adjunct to surgery in patients with brain tumours. In just the same way that CT was a massive advance over plain X-rays of the skull in visualising tumours, radiotherapy techniques are undergoing a transformation with increasing ability to focus the beam onto the tumour, enabling higher doses to be delivered without affecting the surrounding normal brain. New radiotherapy methods such as proton beams promise to refine this process further and improve our ability to treat brain tumours whilst causing less damage.

Other well-known medical imaging techniques are also starting to be used for treatment. Ultrasound scanning, most commonly known for imaging babies developing in the womb, is also being used at high power to treat fibroids in the womb. Furthermore, physicists have found out how to make ultrasound beams pass through the skull, providing the potential for using ultrasound to treat brain tumours.

So, in the field of imaging and its related treatment techniques there is clearly much to be both optimistic and excited about. Maybe the hand-held device for immediate diagnosis and treatment is not yet available, but a whole array of devices are under development and evaluation which will make the diagnosis and treatment of brain tumours easier and more effective, and cause fewer side effects.

Clinical trials for cancer – exploiting our potential

Philip Johnson

ou will have heard or seen in the media a steady stream of reports concerning new discoveries that have the potential to allow a better understanding of disease processes or earlier diagnosis, particularly in my field, cancer. The reports often stem from advances in molecular biology, a relatively new branch of science that has gained prominence since the sequencing of the human genome. After the announcement of the advance, it is revealed that its 'translation' into a new treatment or diagnostic test remains a long way off …

The journey from the concept of a new treatment to its integration into clinical practice is long and trying, often taking more than ten years and 'many are called but few are chosen'. Before any new treatment or diagnostic test can enter clinical practice, researchers have first to show that it is safe, or at least that any adverse safety issues are outweighed by its benefits, and that it really does 'what it says on the tin', for example, shrinks a tumour. By doing so it may actually help patients to survive longer. This process, the 'final common pathway' of drug or test development, is the area of clinical trials wherein patients are treated with the new agent or a new combination of treatments, in a systematic and scientific way, so as to understand how best to use them and how well they work.

Ultimately, a 'controlled' trial usually has to be set up in which the new treatment is compared with the current standard of care. Only in this way can we determine if the new approach is a genuine advance. Such trials require large numbers of patients – certainly several hundred, sometimes several thousand – in order to generate credible measures of efficacy and form the foundation of all of the current medical practice, known as 'evidence based medicine'. The term 'evidence based' distinguishes proven treatments from those that doctors (and often the public) 'get the impression' work. Rigorous clinical trials have often shown that such impressions are misleading or false.

It is not my aim to describe the methodology behind clinical trials; suffice it to say the journey is complex and expensive. A pharmaceutical company may spend billions of pounds on developing a single drug and an individual trial may cost tens of millions of pounds. And when doctors in academia or hospital practice set up trials (so-called academic trials as opposed to pharmaceutical company-sponsored trials) to find the best way of using these new agents, we are still usually talking of hundreds of thousands of pounds. The structures that have to be in place to set up, run and analyse these trials are vast and range from the process of patients giving consent to enter trials and receive appropriate information, through to identification of funding, satisfying regulatory agencies and ethics committees and the involvement of a whole raft of experts in the fields of statistics, pharmacology, nursing, trials management and medical doctors. Much of this work is done by 'big' Pharma but a significant portion is undertaken by the clinical academics, and it is here that I have considerable optimism.

The very concept of the clinical trial originated in the UK with Sir Austin Bradford Hill's work in the 1940s that provided the first real evidence for the value of streptomycin in tuberculosis. Patients generally appreciate being part of a trial, but the infrastructure to run one is now so complex that in most countries only a tiny percentage of patients actually enter a trial, typically much less than 5%. Unless patients undergoing cancer treatment are entered into clinical trials, we do not learn any useful lessons from their experience and there are no advances. The position is simple: no clinical trials, no progress, no bringing new treatments to the clinic – we stay where we are.

However, in the UK over the last decade, the figure for patients entering trials has soared to well over 10% and this country clearly leads the field from an international perspective. The UK has everything set up to be the best place in the world to run trials, with consequent 'wealth and health' benefits. This development was no accident but resulted from a concerted effort of several people, particularly Professor Peter Selby (in his former role as Director of the National Cancer Research Network), with strong support from the Department of Health.

Despite these advances, we need to recognise that progress is still under threat. The regulatory system set up to safeguard patients' interests is now being implemented in a way that risks slowing the process down to a trickle, decreasing the morale of all involved in clinical trials and increasing the costs of trials to the extent that we can do less and less. But if a better risk-based regulatory system can be developed, then there is no reason why the UK should not lead the world in this crucial area of medical research.

Haematological malignancies – the promise of translational medicine

Charles Craddock

aematological malignancies provide a valuable example of the huge clinical potential of novel pharmacological and immunotherapeutic therapies in oncology. In the last decade tyrosine kinase inhibitors, epigenetic agents, proteasome inhibitors, monoclonal antibodies, cord blood transplantation and donor lymphocyte infusion have all become established therapeutic options in the management of leukaemias, myeloma and lymphoma.

This has resulted in improved survival for certain patients with haematological malignancies and highlights the enormous clinical potential of biologically targeted therapies. Despite these advances, the outcome for the majority of adults with haematological malignancies is still unsatisfactory and the majority of patients are destined to die of relapsed or resistant disease.

The advent of novel drug and transplant therapies therefore presents an exciting opportunity to improve the outcome of patients whose outcome with conventional chemotherapy would be very poor, so there is a compelling clinical rationale for the establishment of a trials infrastructure which allows the future rapid testing and development of novel agents in haematological malignancies in a co-ordinated portfolio of early phase clinical trials.

Currently recruitment to early phase clinical trials of new drugs is often slow and this significantly hampers the development of novel therapies. Experience has demonstrated that there are three core requirements required in order to ensure the delivery of high quality early phase trials in haemato-oncology. The first is a large patient catchment area in order to ensure rapid patient recruitment to clinical trials of novel agents. The second requirement is a complex clinical infrastructure of research nurses, trial co-ordinators and statisticians, allowing new treatments to be safely assessed in patients with advanced phase disease. Finally, a strong scientific team is needed to assess the biological activity of novel agents under trial.

Probably the most important reason underlying the continued modest level of recruitment to early phase trials in haemato-oncology in the UK is the absence of a suitable clinical trials network with access to sufficient numbers of patients in order to allow rapid trial recruitment. There is therefore an urgent need to fund a network of haemato-oncology trial units with the aim of creating an internationally competitive portfolio of early phase haemato-oncology trials in the UK.

It is proposed to address this problem by developing a network of early phase trial centres based in leukaemia units in major metropolitan areas within the UK. These centres will work together as a Therapy Acceleration Consortium (TAC). The TAC will serve to allow recruitment to early clinical trials from a catchment area of more than 20 million, thereby ensuring rapid completion of early phase trials and fast-tracking the introduction of novel therapies for patients with haematological malignancies.

The TAC will work to prioritise rapid recruitment to high-quality early phase clinical trials in haemato-oncology. It will do this by facilitating collaboration between a network of busy clinical programmes within large metropolitan centres and high-quality basic science laboratories.

It is anticipated that a number of benefits will accrue from the establishment of a haemato-oncology TAC. One is rapid recruitment to a coherent programme of early phase clinical trials in haemato-oncology, whilst integration of basic science into early phase clinical trials will allow the identification of biomarkers of response and identification of novel targets. This will also allow confirmation of in vivo biological activity of targeted and biological therapies.

A further benefit will be the timely delivery of early phase clinical trials, which will hasten assessment of the clinical activity of novel drugs, allowing them either to be fast-tracked into later phase licensing studies or jettisoned with confidence. At the same time, data generated by the TAC will assist the process of National Institute for Clinical Excellence (NICE) approval and answers a recent request at government level for more high-quality activity data on novel agents.

Economic modelling and experience of the impact of the establishment of a Leukaemia Centre in Birmingham predict that the establishment of the TAC will result in the creation of in excess of 500 new jobs in the biomedical sector and the creation of at least five start-up companies. The creation of an internationally competitive haemato-oncology trials network will also assist delivery of HM Treasury's ambition to develop a knowledge-based economy in the UK with particular strength in the biopharmaceutical and biotechnology sectors.

It is increasingly recognised that patients are currently failing to benefit from the billions of pounds which have been invested into basic medical and scientific research. Consequently the UK's potential to be a world leader in translational medicine is not being fully realised. Previous attempts to increase early phase trial activity in haemato-oncology have been hampered by the absence of a functioning network of leukaemia units with access to the necessary population base required for rapid patient recruitment. The simple initiative of establishing the TAC will create an internationally competitive early phase trial network. Without this co-ordinated initiative the UK would miss an historical opportunity to take a global lead in translational studies in haemato-oncology.

Biopharmaceuticals – transforming disease management

Barbara Conway

I believe that the discovery, development and delivery of new medicines will provide effective therapies for some of those complex diseases for which we have no current effective treatment.

During the limited days of sunshine encountered in England so far this summer, I was lucky enough to be attending my sons' football training when I felt that familiar tingle on my lips and started to apply some Zovirax® (aciclovir) cold sore cream. As you may know, a five year-old is an inquisitive being so I was subjected to the usual 'What are you doing?', followed by the inevitable 'Why?'. I explained how if I put this cream on my lips, I could (hopefully) prevent development of a cold sore. This was followed by much discussion and debate between the younger children and their older siblings.

Not one of the children, including a diverse population up to the age of 14, knew what a cold sore was. I remember being plagued as a child and teenager. At the first sign of sun, a cold, any illness really, the virus would be triggered and I was subjected to the inevitable breakout. Now I can just nip to the supermarket and buy a cream that, if applied early enough, can prevent the eruption or at least accelerate healing.

It was only 50 years ago that the first licensed antiviral drug, 5-iodo-22 -deoxyuridine, was synthesised. The introduction of this and other antivirals initiated a new era in antiviral therapy, with Gertrude B Elion being awarded the 1988 Nobel Prize in Medicine, partly for the development of aciclovir. Less than 30 years later, it is available in a cream form in the supermarket and antiviral therapies are now marketed for treatment of herpes simplex virus, varicella zoster virus, HBV, HCV and influenza A infections – although almost half of the current antiviral agents are for treatment of HIV infections.

Though the rapid development of antiviral drugs has been partly due to the AIDS epidemic, it is an example of how quickly technology, the industry and our expectations for effective therapy can change over a short period. A pre-exposure prophylactic approach is also being proposed for HIV prevention, and science advances at such a rate that drug delivery is now exploring how to exploit viruses to deliver complex molecules into target cells.

However, the way new therapies come about in the future may be somewhat different. The decline in the market for so-called blockbuster drugs has driven a change in focus for the pharmaceutical industry to speciality drugs in niche indications rather than the development of drugs to treat common disorders. The pharmaceutical market is likely to undergo more significant changes over the next few years with inspiration and innovation being driven by the biotechnology market.

With the rapid expansion of technology associated with pharmaceutical development such as computer modelling and high throughput screening used in the biological drug discovery and screening processes, there is the potential to treat complex conditions that are currently not amenable to therapy with conventional drugs. Judging by the impact past developments such as antivirals and antibiotics have had on public health, the rate at which discoveries are being made should herald unprecedented advances in therapy of disease.

Indications with a high chronic disease burden and toll on public health that will benefit from developments in biological therapies include metabolic and autoimmune disorders. Cancer diagnoses are also dependent on biologic drugs, mainly monoclonal antibodies and other therapeutic proteins. These molecules are tumour-specific and improvements in drug particle target efficacy will be key drivers for their success. The tumour targeting potential of these entities will impact on the diagnosis of cancer and development of personalised medicines. Healthcare service provision will also need to adapt to the requirements of personalised medicine, enabling provision for early warning or genetic risk factor screening.

Such information will ultimately impact on the accuracy of selection of appropriate medication for particular patients. Because people differ in their response to drugs, an adverse response to medication is currently a major cause of death or hospitalisation, even when it is appropriately prescribed and administered. However, unprecedented levels of research into pharmacogenetics and pharmacogenomics over the past decade aimed at designing personalised, genetically based therapies for prevention and treatment of disease, have failed to deliver advances that live up to the early hype.

The application of pharmacogenetics is a better approach than the current empirical nature of drug therapies and although challenges and questions do exist, these are not insurmountable. Although the growth in biopharmaceuticals may completely transform disease management and potentially eradicate some diseases, it will also create major resource problems and urgent ethical dilemmas. It is unlikely that many medications will be tailored specifically to individuals; what is more likely is that understanding the underlying mechanisms will lead to improved design and selection of new compounds and that it will be possible to detect polymorphism in gene expression that may affect responses to highly targeted therapies.

The future must offer a more holistic approach, where the information gained by pharmacogenomic profiling is combined with the vast knowledge from conventional medicine to produce more rational therapies. As the body of knowledge and understanding grows, we can make more informed decisions.

Exact predictions, especially in the current climate, are difficult. Nevertheless, as more genomic tools become available and some form of personalised medicine becomes more likely, there is unprecedented potential for preventing or delaying the development of particular complex conditions.

Process monitoring of treatment – taking centre stage

Richard Lilford

eople talk of the heroic phase of medicine being the 1940s and 1950s, the period when life-saving new treatments came into play that would revolutionise medical care – heart surgery, chemotherapy, antibiotics, to name but a few. This was followed by a period where technology was introduced to the health service and just could not be assimilated. Costs were too high, medical providers were uncertain how to best use this new technology and it was difficult to filter those beneficial treatments from the unnecessary and even harmful. Grommets were put in ears, wisdom teeth removed and tonsillectomies carried out routinely and often unnecessarily. Fifteen years after the discovery that heart attack patients could be discharged if given the right medicine, this still was not the norm. The uptake of new advances was haphazard and those in play were frequently not used properly or safely, so often only small incremental improvements were made.

The NHS has all too often been given a bad press: mortality has too often been taken as a measure of quality of care and wrongly so; league tables are misleading and patients do not trust them. This has lead to institutional stigma, juggling and even falsifying figures to make care appear better than this method of analysis shows. Because the signal to noise ratio is bad, mortality is not a good diagnostic test for how good medical care really is.

Now clinical epidemiology has become infinitely harder. We have entered a time where health practitioners are scrutinised at every turn and it has become more difficult to test potentially beneficial treatments. This, however, is a necessary artefact of a glut of new treatments. Patient safety and financial and ethical factors are inevitably at the forefront of any clinical trial and it has now become even harder to find those new treatments which might give the spectacular results that every physician would hope for.

We are entering the 'sunset phase', where success has limited the extent of further improvements. Huge inroads have already been made in the treatment of cardiac disease and cancer and now advances may boil down to merely improving or extending a patient's life by a few months, so the cost-benefit analysis has to be considered. We are perhaps victims of our own success. The game is more marginal and the cost-effectiveness of new treatments more difficult to prove.

Optimistically, our economy is now richer, we have more consultants than ever before and the proportion of money being spent on healthcare has dramatically increased. The humanity of care has also improved. It is astonishing how patients were treated 30 years ago – the NHS has become much more person centred. As technology too continues to improve, we are better able to handle it. Improvements are only taken up when they replace something of less value and if a treatment is not warranted it does not come into use. Big steps have been taken to ensure a more rational approach to new technology and treatments, and more attention is paid to safe practice.

There is no glib solution for measuring the quality of care but, fortunately, analysis by measurement of process is taking centre stage. This involves assessing whether or not patients are receiving the correct treatment and is easy to test. For example, it is easy to measure if a patient with pneumonia receives antibiotics within three hours, or how quickly someone with a blood clot gets anti-clotting medicine, so finding a problem with the process is simple and faults can easily be corrected. Process monitoring will be cheaper and easier, bringing with it inevitable improvements.

Although advances in medicine are now less dramatic, there is one area where huge advances can be made: when it comes to the brain, breakthroughs are still waiting to happen. Alzheimer's and mental illness are the front-runners in terms of where advances can be made.

The future also holds great hope. Computerisation of clinical notes means not only a more organised and more efficient system but also the prospect that patient care will become safer. Interactive elements mean the nurse or physician will be informed by text or other digital methods if medicine has not been given or a treatment might need changing. With better clinical governance, quality will inevitably improve.

The translation of basic biological discoveries to the treatment of disease is also now happening. The treatment of breast cancer, for example, is changing rapidly: oestrogen receptors and growth factors on the cell surface can be identified and taken into account and medicine tailored to each individual patient. The advancement of molecular biology and impact of clinical care mean that tailoring medicine is now fast becoming a reality.

With patient care and its monitoring vastly enhanced, more advanced treatments and technology and scientific information at our fingertips we cannot help but be optimistic that healthcare in this country will continue to improve.

CHAPTER 2

Changing bodies

The biology of ageing – routes to solve the puzzle

Helen Griffiths

I am optimistic that the knowledge gained through research into the basic biology of ageing will bring us to solutions that prevent what is considered to be an inevitable age-associated decline in health.

Only 100 years ago the typical life expectancy of a woman living in the UK was 50 years and that of a man was 46 years. This compares poorly with today's statistics where the average person lives to 81 (woman) and 77 (man) years of age, with more than 90% of adult deaths occurring after the age of 65. These changes have arisen primarily due to improvements in public health and the resulting control of infection, and they mean that lifespan is extended way beyond the age limit for reproduction.

Human physiology has adapted to preserve health and genetic integrity until maximum reproductive age is reached and to conserve energy for circumstances when food may become scarce, but hormonal loss and energy conservation may be less beneficial as we age. So the pay-off against an increase in lifespan has been that health span does not follow suit: rather than sudden death from infection, which was the major cause of death experienced in the 1900s, UK statistics show that in 2000 women will typically experience the last 9.1 years of their life with a chronic, debilitating illness (for men it is 6.8 years).

Typical of these conditions are the major UK killers, cancer and cardiovascular disease, and those chronic diseases that can be considered the consequences of biological ageing. Dementias present more insidious degenerative brain conditions that will become more common in the population as average life expectancy increases. Data from the Alzheimer's Society reports that 700,000 people live with dementia in the UK and that dementia risk doubles with each five-year age group.

At present, each chronic disease condition is identified and treated independently after it has developed. A plausible question is: 'Can increases in knowledge of the biological processes of ageing lead to strategies that prevent the onset of chronic debilitating disease?' The next few paragraphs describe evidence that supports this idea and provide a source of optimism for our health in old age.

Many theories have been proposed to explain the ageing process and they principally revolve around two phenomena: intrinsic effects that are pre-programmed into cells and extrinsic effects that arise from the environment in which an organism develops and lives. Of course, the truth is likely to lie as somewhere between the two and indeed Jeanne Louise Calment, the longest lived person known who died in 1997 aged 122, was exposed to an important extrinsic ageing factor, cigarette smoke – and smoked until the age of 117! Genetic make-up is estimated to contribute approximately 25% to overall age span and previously it was considered that only modification to extrinsic factors may be manipulated (though whether this is still the case is a matter of current debate).

In 1956, Denham Harman proposed that free radicals were major contributors to the ageing process. Free radicals can be produced as by-products during normal metabolic processes, and their production tends to increase with age as the integrity of metabolic processes in the mitochondria becomes less efficient. These radicals are very unstable (existing for less than a microsecond) and highly reactive, showing little selectivity in damage to cellular components. Production of oxygen free radicals by mitochondria can be limited by reducing the rate of metabolism and this observation underpins studies designed to investigate the benefits of caloric or dietary restriction on health span.

It is clear that restricting the calorie intake of organisms – including yeast, water flea, fish, nematode, insect, rodent and monkey – from 'birth' can improve lifespan and also health span, with a reduction in incidence of age-associated cancer in rodents even when the dietary restriction is imposed in adulthood. The reduction in disease incidence is associated with less damage to proteins and DNA caused by oxygen free radicals. There is a critical balance between the oxygen that is needed for life and its contribution to ageing.

Can such findings be translated to human health? The calorie paradigm has not been tested out under the same well-controlled laboratory conditions on human subjects as with rodent studies and may bring with it unknown health problems. Also, such experiments are not easy to undertake and this highlights one of the problems with studying ageing in humans – it takes many years to complete and humans will continue to live in uncontrolled environments during studies. Instead, epidemiological studies have shown associations between calorie restriction and health outcomes but cannot prove causation.

An example of this can be found in Japan, where the average calorie intake is 17% lower than the European diet and health and lifespan is increased. However, such studies cannot take into account genetic differences in addition to the many other lifestyle differences that exist between Japan and Europe. Nevertheless, limited numbers of short-term studies (up to two years in duration) have reported that lowering caloric intake can increase lifespan and reduce the risk of atherosclerosis and inflammation, which in turn are likely contribute to the decrease the incidence of cardiovascular diseases and cancer.

Of course, the most obvious effect of calorie restriction is weight loss. Indeed, excessive weight and obesity with visceral adiposity are increasingly considered as inflammatory conditions that increase the risk of type 2 diabetes (in which cells are resistant to insulin) and cardiovascular diseases. Inflammation is tightly linked to enhanced production of oxygen-free radicals from the mitochondria and from enzyme activity that is required as part of the normal anti-bacterial killing armoury of inflammatory cells. By whichever means (reduced inflammation, lower insulin levels or lower oxygen free radical production), weight reduction can reduce the risk, incidence and severity of major chronic diseases that underlie old age, offering an attainable solution to prolonging health span.

What is the likely compliance for the 20% calorie reduction in older adults that would be needed for an extended health span? Many older adults may be persuaded by arguments for improved health, but socioeconomic status and education are the major indicators for poor health in old age. Adults in the richest area can expect to live 23 years longer than adults in the poorest area, when comparing postcode sector areas, with the major indicator for shortened lifespan being cardiovascular disease.

Instead, pharmacological interventions that address some of the common pathways of accelerated biological ageing that are dependent on improving metabolic function could present an effective means to prolong the health span that may be accessible to wider populations, although such investigations are only at early stages. One example of this is from studies with the micronutrient present in red wine, resveratrol. Health span benefits such as increased insulin sensitivity and improved movement have been reported in obese mice treated with resveratrol. These effects are considered to be due to effects on a target protein family named the sirtuins that have multiple roles in cellular stress resistance, genomic stability, tumourigenesis and energy metabolism.

However, a better understanding of the targets of this intervention, as well as improved knowledge about the common underpinning causes of age-related decline and disease, is essential – for example, what doses of resveratrol will be needed? Is it dangerous to humans at the levels required to have an anti-ageing effect? At what stage in life could it be effective? Will it interfere with other physiological processes? Are other ageing pathways able to circumvent the benefits of resveratrol in humans? Only when these and other questions have been answered can we evaluate whether the health-preserving benefits of resveratrol can be translated to improved health span for humans.

In summary, the routes to solve the puzzle of ageing are being mapped and appear close to leading to solutions that slow age-related decline. It has been estimated that ageing-related health problems cost British taxpayers more than £50 billion a year, and investment in understanding the basic biology of ageing may reduce frailty and disability at all ages for this and future generations.

Rheumatoid arthritis – does time matter?

Chris Buckley, Andrew Filer and Karim Raza

Imagine you wake up one morning and you feel so much pain and stiffness in your joints that every movement is agony. You can no longer dress or wash yourself without help, let alone drive to work. Your GP refers you urgently to a rheumatologist, who tells you that you have arthritis but, though very reassuring, says that even with the results of blood tests, she does not yet know which type of arthritis you have. For the moment your doctors can only offer very general treatment until your arthritis changes to involve more joints in a particular pattern, or until other tests such as X-rays show specific features, which may take months to show up. Distressingly, your rheumatologist cannot tell you whether the arthritis will get better on its own or remain, changing your life forever.

This is the scenario that greets new patients with inflammatory arthritis such as rheumatoid arthritis, who make up 1% of our population. The truth is that we are still very poor at predicting both diagnosis and severity of arthritis in patients presenting to arthritis clinics. Frustratingly, new data from studies looking at treatment of RA in the early stages suggest that very early treatment has the real potential to switch off disease completely, ie to induce disease remission. How can we resolve the problem that currently the best predictor of persistent disease in patients with early arthritis is time? Would we wait as long to intervene in patients with breast lumps or prostate abnormalities as we do in our patients with arthritis?

The last two decades have seen important advances in our understanding of the incidence, treatment and outcome of patients with early rheumatoid arthritis. It is now clear that such patients benefit from early referral and that the outcome of assessment by a rheumatologist is improved by the early introduction of disease modifying anti-rheumatic drugs (DMARDs). With appropriate therapies, it is possible to delay or even prevent evolution of patients with undifferentiated arthritis into rheumatoid arthritis and/or induce remission in a substantial proportion of these patients.

However, optimal management and treatment is often not delivered. This may be due to late presentation of the patient to their GPs, delayed referral to hospital, or reluctance on the part of the physician and/or the patient to adopt an aggressive approach to treatment at the beginning of symptoms. Given the tremendous progress in our understanding of how to image joints, and understand the inflammatory process that occurs in inflamed tissues, we are optimistic that in the near future there will be an individualised treatment plan for each patient with rheumatoid arthritis, as currently occurs for patients with cancer

Renewing eyes – eye focus restored

James Wolffsohn

Whether you are religious or not, you cannot help being in admiration of nature. The eye, my field of specialisation, is less than 3cm in diameter, yet despite our advances in optical technology, we are still far from replicating its ability. However, as we improve our understanding of how nature designed things to be, we become better able to restore the wonders of natural vision as the body ages or becomes diseased.

The eye grows from its development in the foetal tissue to teenage years. As it grows, the optical components and eye length adapt to optimise the clarity of our distant vision, with eye focus allowing a wide range of clear distances. Refractive errors have become increasingly more common, in particular short sight (myopia), where the eye continues to grow beyond its optimal size. In East

Asia, the prevalence of myopia is now around 80%. This eye growth has been linked to our more studious indoor environment as well as having some genetic component.

Recent studies have suggested the drive to eye growth comes from our side vision, which often remains blurred when we look at close objects in our central visual field. Advances in refractive correction, which can be tailored to an individual's optical distortions, are showing promise in being able to slow abnormal eye growth, which if large enough can cause cracks in the photoreceptor layers of the eye, permanently damaging vision.

When we are young, the crystalline lens inside our eye is flexible like a rubber ball and can be stretched by the muscles around the inside of the eye (ciliary muscle). The change in shape of the lens allows us to focus on both distant and near objects. However, the lens continues to grow throughout life, creating new layers (similar to the structure of an onion). These additional layers make the lens stiffer with time and therefore it becomes harder for the muscles to change its shape. This is noticeable by as early as ten years of age and most people require reading glasses by their mid-forties. If we live long enough, the crystalline lens eventually becomes cloudy. This is known as a cataract and it can be removed by surgery.

Cataract surgery was developed by ancient civilizations such as the Egyptians, the Chinese and people of the Indus Valley. The opaque crystalline lens was dislodged from the visual axis by a technique known as 'couching', leaving the eye requiring a high power lens to see clearly at a single distance. Harold Ridley was an eye surgeon at St Thomas' Hospital in London at the end of the Second World War. He noted that shattered plane windscreen fragments that had imbedded themselves in the eye were not 'rejected' by the body. Hence he developed the first crystalline lens replacement, the intraocular lens (IOL), with the first operation performed around 1950. These implants were rigid, so they did not restore eye focus; but they could correct vision, enabling patients to see clearly at a single distance without the need for spectacles.

Cataract surgery at this time involved a very large incision across the cornea (the 'window' of the eye) without the use of an operating microscope. The surgery has developed significantly over the last 60 years and over

300,000 operations are performed each year on the NHS. Current techniques involve the creation of a small, self-sealing incision through which a probe is used to break up and remove the cataract in the centre of the crystalline lens using ultrasound waves. The capsule (shell) of the crystalline lens, which is attached to the muscles that control eye focus, is preserved and the replacement IOL is injected through a small opening into this capsule.

Over the past decade our ability to measure the precise dimensions of the eye have improved, allowing much more accurate calculation of the optimum IOL power to implant. IOLs are now available with advanced optical aspheric and multifocal designs to enhance the quality of vision through the lens. Some have also had blue or violet light-blocking filters incorporated to protect the retina (the 'film' of the eye) from damaging light.

Advances in imaging and recording technology, such as magnetic resonance imaging, have provided evidence that the ciliary muscle remains active throughout life, confirming that the decrease in eye focus is principally due to hardening of the crystalline lens. Consequently, attempts have been made to design IOLs that will restore eye focus. The first generation of these 'bionic' lenses, already available on the market, are designed to move forward in the eye in response to eye muscle forces on their hinges. Our research and that of other groups shows that this approach restores limited eye focus and the effect decreases with time. Designs currently being trialled include dual IOLs on springs that move apart with attempted eye focus and injectable IOLs that replace the hardened crystalline lens following cataract removal.

The problem of 'renewing eyes' is a process that involves translational, multi-disciplinary research – a continuous redesign, laboratory and clinical assessment cycle. New materials and production technology have been developed, surgical implantation techniques have been perfected and the IOLs have been tested in eyes for safety and performance. We have been involved in the development of new ways to assess eye focus to determine how well focusing IOLs perform and better to understand nature's eye focus mechanisms for 'bionic' implants to mimic.

New technology is beginning to allow patients to have their eye focus restored and to see clearly without the need for refractive correction such as glasses. First generation focusing IOLs are not available on the NHS due to their higher cost. Should patients be offered the option of having an advanced IOL for a 'top-up' fee rather than having to go private for both the IOL and cataract surgery? This may go against the ethos of the NHS, but one cannot envisage the NHS paying for these IOL developments with so many other health-improving treatments demanding its limited resources.

However, eye focus is lost mid-life, so why should focusing IOL not be implanted at this stage so that patients can be spectacle-free and will never develop an age-related cataract or need to have to have an operation at a time when other age-related health issues often increase the risks? Conversely, no operation is without risk and is that worth taking in a healthy eye whose lack of focus can be compensated for by spectacles or contact lenses? Despite 'bionic' IOL implants perhaps being seen as of only 'cosmetic' advantage in the developed world, in developing countries where affordable spectacles are often hard to come by, they could restore livelihoods.

Thus do advances in science open social debate. Nevertheless, rapid advances in medical technology offer great promise for overcoming ageing through mimicking nature. Unravelling the secrets of nature offers many challenges for future generations of researchers in many disciplines – and therefore many opportunities for fruitful collaboration.

Oral and dental diseases – a targeted biological approach

Iain Chapple and Tony Smith

Oral and dental diseases are the most prevalent chronic human diseases and affect most of the population at some stage during their lives. They can have profound effects on physiological function, including speech and mastication, quality of life and nutrition, often with greatest impact on the elderly. Periodontal (gum) disease is also an established independent risk factor for adverse diabetes outcomes and cardiovascular disease, especially stroke. In fact, its inflammatory effects can be measured in the systemic circulation.

Although the treatment of this is relatively straightforward, traditional diagnostic and treatment approaches for oral diseases have depended upon the use of the dental probe and mirror, the high speed turbine and the scalpel. For some, this has been a daunting experience! However, we are now moving into a new era where our knowledge of the biological processes underlying oral and dental diseases is being exploited for novel diagnostic and therapeutic purposes which will have a significant impact upon patients' experience as well as the efficacy of dental treatment.

Probing the softness of decayed dental hard tissues is now being superseded by techniques such as quantitative fluorescent monitoring of tissue structural changes, allowing a new level of diagnostic sensitivity for dental caries. The genomic, metabolomic and proteomic era (metabolomics involves the study of chemical fingerprints left behind by cellular processes and proteomics is the large-scale study of proteins) has opened an array of possibilities for saliva as a non-invasive and easily accessible diagnostic medium.

Saliva contains gingival crevicular fluid, which carries with it a fingerprint of a patient's general health, as well as products derived from the local inflammatory-immune response to the microbial biofilm. The development of near-patient salivary diagnostic tests for HIV infection and drugs of abuse is already reality, and bottom-up proteomics approaches are under investigation to identify panels of salivary biomarkers for oral as well as systemic diseases.

Inflammation is the major killer in the developed world and the body's failure to resolve inflammation is the root cause of many chronic diseases. Oral diseases are no different, and the majority of tooth loss arises from perpetuation of inflammation in the pulpal or periodontal tissues. Thanks in part to oral and dental research, the discovery of novel pro-resolving lipid mediators (lipoxins, resolvins and protectins) is leading the way in exploiting naturally active inflammation-resolving pathways. Local manipulation of inflammatory processes has tremendous potential for maintaining tooth vitality and preventing progressive destructive periodontal diseases. At the same time, complementary strategies to harness such approaches with novel regenerative therapies offer great opportunities for more effective management of disease.

Our understanding of the cellular and molecular processes responsible for tooth development is paving the way for the introduction of exciting novel dental tissue regenerative therapies and points the way to bioengineering a whole tooth. During formation of the dental hard tissues, we are not only forming an organ structurally suited to its masticatory role but also laying down an exquisite matrix in which bioactive signalling molecules are sequestrated and fossilised. These bioactive molecules can survive in an active state under these fossilised conditions for many decades of life and may be released at times of dental decay, initiating tissue regeneration.

Exploitation of these molecules for both stimulation of natural regenerative processes and development of novel biomaterials will allow future dental restorations to become an integral part of the tooth, replacing the present inert filling materials which depend on adhesion for retention. This also provides a stepping stone towards whole tooth tissue engineering where our knowledge of dental stem cells and associated developmental events can be harnessed to bioengineer all of the components of a tooth, as well as the supporting bone and attachment apparatus. Emphasis on maintenance of tooth vitality after treatment will herald a major advance for our patients' experiences of dentistry.

Clearly, a targeted biological approach to dentistry has the potential to improve diagnosis and treatment outcomes dramatically. The wide-ranging benefits to the whole population provide us with a very positive vision for the future.

Membrane proteins – crucial drug targets

Roslyn Bill

We still have much to learn about ourselves and the world around us. I am confident that humankind has the capacity to keep generating new knowledge through scientific endeavour and that this knowledge will enable us to provide solutions which can positively impact on our quality of life. I am also confident that an education will soon be considered incomplete without the scientific literacy that promotes critical thinking rather than reacting to speculation, hype or media frenzy. Maybe then future politicians will have the ability to implement the results of scientific research for the good of all.

Being a professional scientist is a great privilege that requires optimism. I often wonder whether I am a scientist because I believe I can challenge the status quo and improve upon it or whether my optimism has arisen from my scientific experience. Whichever it is, I would encourage students of all ages to share this positive outlook with me and to study science.

My own area of scientific interest is focused on proteins, which are crucial to the correct functioning of all living organisms. Proteins have a myriad of functions in cells, ranging from providing their structural integrity to facilitating communication with their surroundings. A special class of proteins, called membrane proteins, sits within the membraneous structures that encompass all cells. These membranes ensure that a cell's contents stay within the cell, with the membrane proteins acting like gatekeepers, allowing substances such as nutrients in – and keeping waste products out – at the right time. These 'gatekeepers' are also the key to how cellular communication works.

It is perhaps not surprising, then, that membrane proteins are crucial drug targets in a wide range of diseases. Because they mediate many key processes in cells during both health and disease, they are already the targets of well over 50% of marketed drugs, a number which is set to rise to over 75% in the coming decades.

Having access to appropriate membrane protein samples for future research underpins many of the modern pharmaceutical industry's strategies for developing new blockbuster drugs. Because they are not naturally abundant, membrane proteins have to be synthetically generated for entry into the drug discovery pipeline. This need for high yields of artificially generated membrane proteins is an enduring challenge in contemporary bioscience.

One solution to the challenge is to synthesise these proteins in simple host cells (so-called 'cell factories') which can be grown on a large scale. In this way, the pure protein can be isolated in quantities much higher than those found in the protein's native human cells. Widely used host cell factories include organisms such as bacteria and yeast cells: in my laboratory we focus on yeast. Traditionally, this process of using cell factories to produce membrane proteins in high yields has been regarded as something of an art form and consequently has remained in the doldrums for decades.

changing bodies

To meet this challenge, my colleagues and I have pioneered the production of membrane proteins in cell factories as a science, thereby challenging the status quo. This approach, based on improved scientific understanding, has resulted in the design of novel cell factories for the reliable production of membrane proteins for the first time.

In the long term, we are optimistic that our findings will feed directly into drug discovery pipelines to benefit an ageing population, who will need new drugs to combat diseases including diabetes, cancer and neurological disorders. It is also our hope that our research will contribute to overcoming diseases such as malaria and viral infection that afflict so many developing nations.

Delaying the effects of ageing – doing something simple

Janet Lord

Increased life expectancy and falling birth rates have had dramatic effects on population demographics and Europe is now the oldest continent in terms of the proportion of the population aged over 65. In the UK there are now over 9,000 centenarians and Buckingham Palace is rumoured to be considering raising the age for receipt of the Queen's birthday telegram from 100 to 105. Moreover, there is little indication that these trends are temporary and average life expectancy is now increasing at a rate of two years per decade, equivalent to five hours a day. Or, put another way, this means that a child born tomorrow has a life expectancy of five hours more than a child born today!

That one in five of the population will be aged over 65 by the year 2020 is a cause for celebration, but not for complacency. Although medical advances have ensured that a greater proportion of the population make it through to the third age of man, they have made less impact upon the quality of life in old age. Age is the most important risk factor for many disabling human diseases, including dementia, cardiovascular disease, non-insulin dependent diabetes and arthritis, and on average men will still be unwell for the last six years of their lives and women for the last 11 years. As the actress Bette Davis once said, 'Old age is no place for sissies'.

With these statistics it may seem rather perverse, or deluded, to hold any degree of optimism towards my old age. What then is the basis for my positive opinion of the prospects of an old age that is enjoyed rather than endured? Put simply, my rosy outlook derives from a change in attitude towards ageing and improved understanding of the processes responsible for ageing. Thus the reluctance of the baby boomer generation to accept that old age heralds an entry into physical and mental decline has coincided with developments in biomedical research that show very clearly that the process of ageing is malleable.

Studies in a wide variety of species, including fruit flies, worms and rodents, have shown that variations in single genes that influence growth, metabolism and the ability to deal with tissue damage (the insulin-IGF-1 pathway) can dramatically extend lifespan. More importantly, in these species extended lifespan was accompanied by retardation of the negative aspects of ageing, including loss of muscle mass, decline in immune function and reduced cognitive function. Very recently genetic studies in humans have revealed that long-lived individuals (those greater than 90 years old) also have a beneficial gene variant of the IGF-1 pathway (the AKT gene), suggesting that the influence of this process upon longevity and health extends to humans. That longevity has a genetic component has been confirmed by studies of twins which have shown that our genes contribute approximately 25% towards lifespan – so a good start to a long life is to choose your parents well!

With 25% of longevity determined by genetics, this still leaves 75% available to be influenced. Biogerontologists have concluded that ageing is a lifelong process and that the health of the individual in old age is influenced by environmental factors such as diet, exercise and stress experienced throughout the life course. Preventing age-related frailty can thus be achieved by appropriate interventions at any stage in life and effort is now being made to develop and validate such interventions.

With respect to diet, research in several organisms has shown that reducing the intake of calories in adults to approximately 25–30% of that required to maintain normal body weight, termed caloric restriction (CR), can extend lifespan by up to 40%. Importantly, the calorie-restricted animals also showed improved health in old age, including reduced levels of heart disease and neurodegeneration. CR appears to have its effects in part by modulating the IGF-1 pathway, but clearly also leads to lifespan extension by other means, including the increased activity of enzymes called sirtuins. The seven known sirtuins have a range of functions that help to reduce the effects of ageing, including repair of damaged DNA and helping the body's cells maintain their energy supply and reduce the production of damaging oxygen radicals, by maintaining the correct functioning of mitochondria (the major providers of energy within the cell).

More recently, studies in a range of species have shown that CR may also work through inhibiting another enzyme, TOR (mammalian Target of Rapamycin), which senses the level of amino acids (constituents of protein) in the diet and regulates protein synthesis and growth. Interestingly, reducing amino acid intake also extends lifespan in yeast, fruit flies and rodents. CR thus appears to have its effects by several routes, many of which involve the body's processes for sensing the availability of food.

CR studies are now ongoing in the US in primates and short-term CR interventions (one to two years) have also been tried in humans. Although it is too early to know whether lifespan will be increased by CR in primates, early indications from this work are that the timing of commencement of CR is important. For example, it is well established that the functioning of the immune system declines with age, resulting in increased susceptibility to infections and poorer vaccination responses in older adults.

Recent reports concerning the ability of CR to delay the age-related loss of immune function have shown that CR applied in juvenile primates was detrimental to immunity and if applied in older adults (equivalent to late middle age in humans) CR had no effect. CR was only beneficial for immunity in old age when applied to young adults. In this sense, Theodore

Roosevelt may have been correct when he said that 'Old age is like everything else, to make a success of it you've got to start young'.

The problem with CR is, of course, that it is unacceptable as a long-term lifestyle choice – who wants to live 40% longer if it is a life spent counting every calorie and avoiding fish and chips! The current obesity epidemic tells us that getting people to adopt even a diet that maintains a healthy body weight is difficult; asking them to live on lettuce leaves for the rest of their lives is thus a non-starter. The search is now on for a CR mimetic – a pill that will give the same effects without the need for a drastic reduction in food intake. This idea may seem fanciful, but two CR mimetics have already been found and have been shown to extend lifespan and reduce age-related disease in rodents.

Early research by Professor Lenny Guarente and Dr David Sinclair at Harvard University revealed that resveratrol, a chemical found in red wine, was able to increase lifespan in yeast. They showed that resveratrol is able to activate sirtuins and in this way is able to extend lifespan. Resveratrol itself is unlikely to be used as a CR mimetic in higher species such as rodents or humans due to its potential for cardiotoxicity at the dose required. However, new chemicals based upon resveratrol have now been synthesised, and these are more potent and can be given at much lower doses that do not produce side effects.

A spin-off company formed by Dr Sinclair to produce the resveratrol analogues (Sirtris Pharmaceuticals) was purchased recently by the pharmaceutical giant GSK for $237 million and is already carrying out clinical trials with these new compounds for the treatment of age-related disease, initially focusing on diabetes. A second CR mimetic that works through inhibiting the TOR enzyme is an antibiotic called rapamycin. Scientists have shown very recently that mice given rapamycin lived much longer. Importantly, if the mice were given the drug in late middle age, the lifespan extending effect was still seen. So even the baby boomer generation may be able to benefit from the new developments in ageing research! In fact, a drug to combat several of the negative effects of ageing may be available in the next decade, rather than the distant future of our grandchildren.

For most people, however, prevention is better than cure and increasingly researchers are focusing their efforts upon ways to maintain health and well-being in old age. The intervention that has come to the fore as one that is practical and will benefit many aspects of health and well-being is exercise. There is now a strong evidence base for the beneficial effects of exercise on cardiovascular function, maintenance of the musculoskeletal system, immunity, mental well-being and cognition. In my own area of immunity, for example, it is well established that older adults do not make an optimum response to vaccinations, leaving them more susceptible to a wide variety of infections such as flu. Less than half of those over 65 having the annual flu vaccination will make enough antibodies in response to the vaccine to give them full protection against the influenza virus. This is not to say that seniors should not have their flu jabs, as these will still give some protection and at the very least will help to reduce the symptoms of the infection.

However, research by Dr Marion Kohut in the US has shown that when older adults undertook an aerobic exercise session lasting 30 minutes at least three times a week for the 12 weeks before a vaccination, they dramatically increased the amount of antibodies produced. Clearly such an exercise regime will be difficult for many older adults and research at Birmingham University is now trying to determine just how little exercise is required in order to improve vaccination responses in older adults. It may be that something as simple as walking briskly to the GP's surgery before the flu jab rather than taking the car or bus may do the trick!

In summary, I fully intend to enjoy old age in good health, achieved by regular exercise (of mind and body) and the company of good friends. Although I may have recourse to help from the latest in pharmaceutical interventions towards the end of my life, I am optimistically aiming for a long life and a short death!

Redox husbandry – intimations of immortality

Adrian Williams

Ageing, fortunately, is neither inevitable 'wear and tear', nor is it genetically programmed. Longevity is remarkably easily manipulated by diet, stress, physical and mental exercise and genetic perturbations that affect energy and information flows and balances. Ageing is on a continuum with evolution and development and is equally shaped by external and internal energy micro-environments whose patterns drive cellular differentiation, function and maintenance. Longevity is, after all, inexplicably increasing in beneficent economies, suggesting the inadvertent removal of environmental constraints.

Until recently scientists have been focusing inwards – on genetics, 'frailty' or 'causative' genes' that appear to cause ageing diseases. These are in part responsible for those diseases associated with ageing, whether dementia, Parkinson's disease, organ failures, autoimmune disease, atherosclerosis, diabetes or cancer. In most cases, given the right cellular environment these genes do not cause trouble: a deleterious mutation, does not mean the ageing disease will take hold. Cancer, for example, is not merely down to a few mutations: something about the whole microenvironment has gone wrong. An already inherited mutation gives the cells a predisposition towards cancer, but not all individuals with cancer genes get the disease: secondary 'epigenetic' factors are required.

Gene hunting is big business. It provides us with relevant information about individual mutations and valuable models for biochemical pathways involved in disease, but it is not the answer to ageing. Finding key frailty genes is helpful, but scientists need to discover exactly what causes the genome to go awry. If we knew what the variant was up to, perhaps as a 'thrifty' gene that was beneficial under earlier ecologies, we would be able to compensate.

Ageing is best seen as a systems failure encompassing many factors but with a common final pathway. These are the elements that influence energy transport, thriving on mainly predictable shocks as long as these are not severe or capricious. Collaborative interplay with our biotic environment has the gene products of our diet and symbionts largely regulating our epigenomes – not purely 'our genetic selves', as previously and anthropocentrically perceived.

The pessimist would perceive the population to be rife with mutations that pre-programme senescence, but this is paranoid thinking. Mutations are not 'designed' to cause disease; rather, they are a genetic response to selection pressures. Evolution has not pre-programmed so called 'causative genes' into the system. Much molecular pathology, such as 'autocarnivory' or the reversions to fermentations seen in cancer tissue, may be homeostatic attempts to correct energy landscapes.

Optimistically, searching for different causes for all ageing diseases may not be necessary; perhaps a single simple cause intervention could be the answer. Correct energy flow to the genes' advantage and ageing diseases might be prevented.

All organisms require energy to survive, produced through oxidation and reduction or redox reactions. However, energy supplies adequate for survival may not always be enough to develop spare capacity for the long haul or to deal optimally with repairs. Such damage to the stability of the genome is important for the maintenance of differentiated tissues and epigenetic 'memory', hard fought for during evolution and again during development.

All cells in our body have the same genome, but they are all different, so the difference must be down to epigenetics. Turning on or off certain genes leads to cell differentiation. This cannot be done internally as the genomes are identical; it has to come from the outside. This may be from the cell's microenvironment, led by the cell next door sending growth factors through, but eventually neighbours run out and co-evolved diet and symbionts call the tune, both supplying energy and information to the cells.

Frailty genes are more likely rare mistakes, and the cell-specific diseases that are responsible for ageing are best seen as side effects, a mismatch of a combination of adaptations earlier on in an individual's life. Ageing is down to energy trade-offs that prioritised growth, development, reproduction and informatics which then take their toll later on. A life-time high – but not too high – energy and information tide may avoid exposing these Achilles heels.

Energetically, the brain is on a tight budget and has to rationalise its energy use, so surviving in the short term becomes a priority, taking its toll later on in life. Ageing diseases are 'side effects' within a thermodynamically run environment. Optimistically, these 'side effects' may be avoided by inserting artificial redox sensors as late-life aids to keep our cells' energy levels in equilibrium.

Stem cells utilise redox energy gradients to drive differentiation that can be affected by anoxia, toxins, infections and physical and mental stresses. The result is that all systems learn epigenetically from experience, building on inherited information, both genetic and epigenetic. If that fails from exposure to redox extremes, anabolic functions are shut down or indulge in dangerous syntheses in order to ensure or control the energy supply – at the price of ageing tissues.

Energy and information input into the brain are interlinked. The frontal-parietal path which gets hit in Alzheimer's disease is the area that young people use when they are thinking about their past or future, the area responsible for prediction and, taken too far, worry. Worry is what the brain does by default and it is metabolically active much of the time, using up a great deal of energy. Similarly, the basal ganglia, which fails in Parkinson's disease, is also an energy thirsty area even when you are inactive. Compared with other parts of the body like muscle, the brain uses a great deal of energy when idling. Calorific, psychological and environmental stress when young put excessive energy demands on the brain to be paid for later in life. So much of our pathology may be homeostatic attempts to correct energy landscapes. Optimistically, we can change outside factors a lot more easily than we can change our own genome.

Will better redox husbandry make us immortal? Perhaps not. Even though some do talk of reversing senescence, we do not have membranes that can withstand radical attack indefinitely. Nevertheless, concentrating not on frailty genes, but removing environmental constraints and investigating robust redox atmospheres, could optimistically enable more positive plastic characteristics to emerge out of our cryptic genetic potentialities and life-long development – so the optimists may be right.

Plastic brains –
making up for lost neurons

Georgina Rippon

Jacques: Last scene of all,
That ends this strange eventful history,
Is second childishness and mere oblivion,
Sans teeth, sans eyes, sans taste, sans everything.

(Shakespeare *As You Like It*, Act 2, Scene 7, 164–167)

The suggestion that 'the first people to live to be 1,000 have already been born' is generally greeted with a shudder of revulsion. It is not normally the economic, environmental and social aspects that first spring to mind in musing on the consequences of this, but the spectre of the ageing body and the demented brain, the regression to Jacques' 'second childishness'. It is assumed that this is true for all of us as we age, not just those suffering from pathologies such as Alzheimer's disease – there is no such thing as 'healthy ageing'.

But cognitive neuroscientists have good news on this front and much cause to be optimistic. Instead of insider knowledge supporting a vision of inevitable neuronal death, cognitive decline and sensory loss, our research now shows that ageing is not the gloomy picture painted by Jacques. In its place we can ponder an encouraging prospect of adaptable brains, cognitive reserves and neural networks with previously undreamed of capacity for compensation and recruitment. We have research models with wonderful titles such as CRUNCH (Compensation-Related Utilisation of Neural Circuits Hypothesis) and STAC (Scaffolding Theory of Ageing and Cognition). Not only that, but if things do start to slip we have a whole array of 'neurocognitive prostheses' to prop up our failing mental faculties.

What has led to this reassessment of what confronts us with the passing of time? In the last decade or so, there has been a conjunction of dramatic developments in how we can study the brain. We can image the 'where, when and what' of brain activity, we have the computational power to manipulate and model the huge data sets that neurocognitive research can generate and we have access to great swathes of research outside our immediate expertise which can inform the interdisciplinarity essential to characterising the problem of the ageing brain – or, indeed, of demonstrating that it does not need to be a problem!

In the past few decades, it has become clear that the representation of the brain as a rigid set of specialist modules, underpinned by fixed groups of nerve cells with no ability to repair and replace themselves, is far from the truth. Similarly, the suggestion that we lose our nerve cells at an alarming rate after about ten years of age has been replaced by evidence that neuronal loss is actually minimal and what changes is the extent and efficiency of the connections between our brain cells, connections that we now know can be enhanced, reorganised or ever replaced.

The brain has powers of adaptability and recovery much greater than we had ever envisaged. This change has had profound implications not only for our understanding of how our brains enable us to do what we do, but especially for our attitude to what happens to our brains (and so to us) as we age.

We have long known that our brains possess a characteristic 'plasticity', the ability to respond adaptively to internal and external demands. Our brains can lay down new connections and form new assemblies, either transiently or permanently, or reorganise circuits in response to structural changes. But we had assumed that this plasticity was the function of the young, developing brain and that, with ageing, we lose this dynamic capacity.

However, recent research has shown that the type of environmental enrichment that can lead to increased density of connections in the developing brain can equally affect (and effect) electrophysiological and chemical connections in the aged brain, encouraging the formation of new connections and protecting those that already exist. It has also been demonstrated in a large-scale, randomised, double-blind control trial that specific types of cognitive training can improve memory and attention in older adults. Similarly, different types of physical activity (such as dancing!) have been shown to be associated not just with decreased rates of cognitive decline but positive improvements in performance.

It has been shown that many people, including the aged, have a striking capacity to show little or no cognitive decline despite quite severe brain pathology. The concept of cognitive reserve has been proposed to explain this phenomenon. This cognitive reserve seems to be based on neural reserve, the underlying efficiency of existing networks (probably determined by genetic factors and/or life experiences such as educational exposure or physical activity) and also on neural compensation – the ability of the brain to enlist alternative strategies, reorganise existing networks and recruit different or alternative networks. It is clear that earlier generations of researchers dramatically underestimated this latter capacity and this proposed model of cognitive reserve: 'compensatory scaffolding' supports a much more cheerful uncoupling of cognitive function from underlying cortical decline.

In spite of this rosy picture, it is clear that eventually hardware deficiencies will catch up with us and our cognitive abilities will be compromised by the deterioration of our brain structures. Over-optimism could take us well beyond the current limits of our research horizons and paint a picture of replacement brains or the reversal/removal of the ageing process altogether. However, research has already shown that our knowledge of brain function can enable the production of 'neurocognitive prostheses', the brain's equivalent of artificial limbs.

This is in addition to the techniques of gene therapy and neural implants that are being pioneered in the treatment of pathological ageing. We can improve language in aphasics by stimulating specific circuits in the brain, we can alter learning by varying the frequencies of brain activity. Just as we can restore motor function by harnessing the activity of the brain's motor cortex, we could restore cognitive function by harnessing cortical activity. More immediately, there are already techniques of 'neurocognitive enhancement', both pharmacological and educational, which have been demonstrated to improve and reverse cognitive decline.

So, if you're an ageing cognitive neuroscientist, things are definitely looking up. What is even more cheering is that the actions required to support and supplement our cognitive and neural reserves can be fun. One study has shown that taking up the tango had significant benefits, not only physical but also cognitive. 'Brainspan to match Lifespan' is the motto. And as optimism has also been shown to be a significant factor in healthy ageing, we can reap the benefits of our own research!

PART 2

The Macrocosm –
Interacting with our world

CHAPTER 3

Living in the natural world

Bio-ethanol production – harnessing plant biomass

Tim Bugg

We face great challenges. Our standard of life is arguably higher than it has ever been, but our modern lifestyle is hungrier than ever before for energy and non-renewable resources, and evidence mounts that man-made carbon dioxide emissions are leading to global warming. A high proportion of items found around the home, and clothes that we wear, contain synthetic man-made materials and fibres whose raw materials originate from oil, but a shortage of fossil fuels threatens the entire petrochemical and chemical industry. What are we to do when the oil reserves run out?

I believe that science will find solutions to these challenges. Throughout human history, scientific innovations have revolutionised the way we live, from the discovery of the steam engine and the internal combustion engine, to the miracles of modern medicine such as penicillin and heart surgery. Such scientific innovations have usually been accompanied by great optimism about science and its impact on society, but today the general public in many Western countries – perhaps influenced by the media's portrayal of the chemical and pharmaceutical industries as villains – forget that behind all new discoveries lie the unremitting efforts of teams of scientists whose only concern is to discover things and make life better for all of us.

In response to the energy crisis, there is general agreement that society should make greater use of renewable energy sources, but new technology is needed to make solar energy and biofuels economically viable and environmentally sustainable. For solar energy, one approach is to mimic the process of photosynthesis that nature uses to convert light into biochemical energy.

Using X-ray crystallography, researchers have been able to establish the three-dimensional structure of the light-harvesting protein (called the photosynthetic reaction centre) from a purple photosynthetic bacterium, *Rhodobacter sphaeroides*, and use the structure to understand the processes of electron transfer involved in light harvesting. Electrochemists have also been able to deposit a thin layer of the plant photosynthetic reaction centre onto gold electrodes, and hence convert light directly into electric current. Other researchers in chemistry are trying to develop completely new, man-made materials that could be used to make solar cells.

Biofuels derived from plant biomass represent another major source of energy. Brazil has produced bio-ethanol by fermentation of glucose from sugar cane since 1976, and its cars are adapted to run on a mixture of petroleum and bio-ethanol. This first generation technology, for bio-ethanol production has been criticised for its environmental impact because of the large amounts of land required for sugar cane harvesting, and the resulting 'food versus fuel' debate has featured in newspapers and on television. However, research on second generation technology has established that it is possible to obtain 'cellulosic bio-ethanol' from the cellulose cell walls that are present in all plants, not just sugar cane.

In order to make this commercially viable, we need to improve the efficiency of the conversion of plant biomass into glucose and devise new methods for the treatment of lignin, an aromatic polymer that is also present in cellulose cell walls. Using biotechnology, researchers have engineered plants with reduced lignin content that give higher yields of bio-ethanol after pulping. Other researchers are using nature's enzymes to break down ligno-cellulose to produce bio-ethanol. Nature has the enzyme catalysts to do these conversions, so I am optimistic that scientists will find new ways to make second generation bio-ethanol production a reality.

Bio-conversion of plant cell walls has other potential bonuses. Their sugar and lignin content can potentially be converted into useful chemicals, which could then be used to make household products and pharmaceutical drugs. Furthermore, the recalcitrant lignin polymer contains aromatic (benzene) rings that are found in many drugs, so if we can find ways to harness plant biomass, we will have renewable sources of valuable chemicals without having to use crude oil.

In the next 20–30 years, I think we will see the development of 'bio-refineries' that produce a range of useful products from biomass, in the same way that oil refineries produce chemicals from oil. We need to use biotechnology to find new solutions to the challenges that face society, whilst at the same time demonstrating that they will not impact adversely on our environment – and I am confident that we shall do so.

Biomass –
harvesting available energy

Tony Bridgwater

This article may appear to be doom and gloom about the prospects for the world and all those who expect and hope to share in its future. But it is important to have some appreciation of the challenges to be faced in order to derive an optimistic view of our future. The challenges are far too complex to be comprehensively covered but need to be outlined in order to justify the final claims.

There can be few who are unfamiliar with the threatened consequences of climate change. The consequences will be dramatic and severe and will affect many aspects of rain, water, temperature and sea levels with different effects in different areas. There are, however, many other consequences of our accelerating development which are already having a profound impact on our future.

Whilst our basic needs can be defined as food, water and shelter, we now expect that these needs will be lavishly supplemented by all the appurtenances that modern society has led us to expect. However, in a finite world with finite resources which are rarely evenly distributed, there are a number of areas or challenges where shortages could have a profound impact on our future, the most important of which are energy, food and water.

We are living in an energy-rich society where energy is considered to have been too cheap for too long and has fuelled our seemingly insatiable appetite for growth. Renewable energy is being promoted as a solution to managing the increasing carbon dioxide (CO_2) levels that are predicted to have profound effects on the future of the world.

There are three fundamental sources of renewable energy: the sun, tides and heat from the earth. The sun provides heat and light that is manifested in several forms: as biomass which can be recovered as food or energy crops; as wind and waves from weather effects which can be recovered usually as electricity; as electricity from photovoltaics; and as heat through solar-thermal devices. This is by far the largest renewable resource. The second source, tides, can be harnessed to produce electricity. This is currently a relatively minor source, as is the third source, heat from the earth's core.

The total solar energy absorbed by the earth is approximately 3,850,000 exajoules per year (exajoule, EJ = 10^{18} joules). In one hour this is approximately the total energy that the world currently uses in one year. Put another way, the amount of solar energy reaching the surface of the planet in one year is twice as much as will ever be obtained from all non-renewable resources of coal, oil, natural gas and mined uranium combined. So energy is available, we just need to find a way of harvesting it.

Of the 3,850,000 EJ per year received by the earth, 30% is reflected and 70% – or 2,695,000 EJ – is absorbed. The largest useable products of this absorbed energy is first biomass, which captures about 3,000 EJ per year through photosynthesis and, secondly, wind, which captures about 2,250 EJ. This should be set against the global primary energy consumption of 484 EJ per year and electricity consumption of 57 EJ per year.

Biomass is thus one of the major renewable resources available to us. A large proportion is not harvested and naturally decays to humus and CO_2 and methane as part of a natural cycle, which was how coal was originally formed. However, some of this biomass is used for food and commodities such as paper, timber and cloth.

Of the three primary renewable energy forms available to us (biomass, electricity and heat) only biomass can provide orthodox transport fuels and the chemicals needed to substitute for oil and gas-derived products. Biomass also absorbs the CO_2 that is increasing and causing global warming, so it is important as a control mechanism as well as being a major source of renewable energy – use of 1 tonne of biomass for energy replaces about 0.5 tonnes oil or gas and about 0.7 tonnes of coal. Although biomass has long been associated with food production, it has recently been recognised as having the potential to provide the largest renewable energy resource of the future, and this has led to concerns over competition.

Fossil fuels will never actually run out: they will just become more difficult and hence more costly to extract, and will be subject to the laws of supply and demand. Some resources such as coal and tar sands have projected lifetimes of hundreds of years, but the consequence of continuing to use fossil fuels without regard for the environment is quite clear. Nuclear is promoted as a more acceptable greenhouse gas energy resource but carries its own problems and is also resource limited.

The increasing interest in renewable energy and particularly in biomass has resulted in the use of food crops for energy, such as production of biodiesel from vegetable oil and bioethanol from wheat, sugar cane and sugar beet. This practice attracts opprobrium for its diversion of essential food away from human needs to energy, which has led to more advanced and more efficient but more expensive technologies to process non-food crops for what are known as second generation biofuels. Biomass is also increasingly used directly for electricity and heat production in many countries, driven by a range of fiscal incentives.

So the competition for land, which is a finite resource, has become a major issue, from destruction of rain forests, which absorb CO_2 and thus mitigate the greenhouse effect, to substitution of energy crops for food crops.

This leads to the second of the major challenges facing us: how much food do we need and how much food can we grow? Food yields (tonnes/hectare, t/ha) have grown considerably in the last 100 years as a consequence of the introduction of artificial or synthetic fertilisers, synthetic biocides and crop development. This is a direct consequence of the availability of (cheap) oil and gas and the inventiveness and imagination of scientists and engineers.

There are, however, some limits as to how much food can be produced. The first theoretical upper limit is based on the availability of energy from sunlight and limits yield to about 50–150 t/ha per year on a dry yield basis depending on latitude. The second theoretical upper limit is the amount of land available to grow crops. The total land area in the world is 148,500,000 square km (14,850 million ha), of which between 13 and 24% is arable (depending on definitions) and less than 40% of this is used for agriculture.

The maximum theoretical world biomass production is therefore very roughly 267,300 million tonnes per year based on current estimates of suitable land availability. In practice, only 5–20% of the theoretical maximum is currently achievable, but this shows that the potential for biomass production is considerably greater than current need for both food and energy. Translating the 3,000 EJ of energy absorbed by biomass mentioned above gives 150,000,000,000,000 million tonnes per year of biomass that is produced globally.

There is general agreement in the literature that the world is capable of producing sufficient food for everyone, even a larger population than at present, and this is clear from the simplistic calculations above. The question of whether there is enough land available both to feed everyone and to provide their energy and consumer needs in the future is not clear, particularly with a growing population.

The future for biomass is wide open, with opportunities for many innovative developments, such as crop improvements through selection and breeding; genetic modification to improve crop and biomass yields and quality; derivation of refined products such as diesel directly from modified algae; and artificial photosynthesis to remove or reduce the theoretical limits to photosynthesis.

The third major challenge arises from the availability of water. Water is life and seems likely to become an issue earlier than any of the other resources considered. An interesting statistic is that 2,000 litres of water are needed to produce 1 litre of milk and 24,000 litres of water are needed to produce 1kg of beef. A significant proportion of the world's water comes either from irreplaceable aquifers (which are by definition not renewable) or from glacier melt – and there is extensive evidence of retreating glaciers and reduced run-off, with some rivers frequently running dry in summer. Even in the UK there are signs of water stress, with concern over water supplies. Without water, crops will fail. Without water or crops there is the potential for human catastrophe of unbelievable proportions.

If resources are finite and cannot be changed, then attention has to be turned to the consumers, ie the world's population. How many people can the world support? What is a sustainable population level? How are we going to reach it?

A recent UN study reviewed possibilities for world population in 2300. Three basic scenarios project a medium case where increased longevity is balanced by changed fertility, giving a relatively unchanged population of around 9 billion in 2300 against a current global population of around 7 billion. The low scenario produces around 2.3 billion and the high 36.4 billion. Fertility is a key parameter in these forecasts. If fertility is maintained at year 2000 levels, this gives a projected population of 244 billion by 2150 and 134,000 billion by 2300. In this scenario, the more developed countries would see their populations decline from 1.2 billion to 0.6 billion.

Population levels and growth and sustainability have been widely studied, with estimates of the maximum sustainable population of the world between 2 and 15 billion, with 2 to 3 billion being the most popular conclusion.

So, in the next 100 years, the world potentially faces food shortages, energy shortages, water shortages, climate change and population growth. What, then, is there to be optimistic about?

Mankind is competitive – if it were not so we would never have developed from animals to express our will and compete for attention and resources.

Mankind is resourceful as evidenced in the myriad of inventions and developments that we enjoy today.

The hope is that the world will retreat from its adversarial attitude and innate competitiveness to recognise the size and scale of the problems properly, working globally to manage them, sensibly and seriously. There is cause for hope in the evidence of global recognition and united contribution to reducing carbon emissions. Further evidence comes from recent Chinese policies on population growth, which appear to have met with such success that the policy has recently been relaxed. So the major countries and the world can, when necessary, deliver solutions.

The previously unimaginable technical developments over the last 150 years provide sufficient evidence to justify an optimistic and positive view of our future. Examples of possible developments include artificial photosynthesis, cold fusion, hot fusion, terraforming unusable landscapes for vegetation and many of the imaginative ideas advocated by science fiction writers.

So I am not just hopeful, but confident and optimistic, that the future of the world is safe – though the pathway there will be rocky and dangerous at times.

Biochar – stabilising world climate

Andreas Hornung

Mankind is facing one of its most significant challenges. Nature is able to survive, as it has been proven in the last 100 million years, but mankind and its habitat are fragile – even if we do not like to look at things in those terms. The global challenges we face are to provide energy and water in order to support nations and their development, and our response to these circumstances will have to lead us to unknown or unexpected solutions.

The sad fact is that the opportunities to sustain an adequate energy supply via high-tech routes are not yet ready to be applied, not because of the technology, but because of international politics. As an interim solution we are looking today for the implementation of biomass as a means of supplying energy. Birmingham city, together with Aston

University and the related research capacities in the region, have therefore established a showcase scenario to bring this to people's attention.

The 'Biothermal valorisation of Biomass process' aims to use biogenic residues like waste wood, sewage sludge, biogas residues, ground service and garden residues to produce heat and power, hydrogen and synthetic natural gas and diesel in order to reduce the carbon dioxide emissions of Birmingham by 60% by 2026. The core installation is a decentralised network of 10 megawatt plants to turn those biomasses via coupled pyrolysis-gasification into synthesis gas.

The products this delivers enable companies and research organisations of the region to apply their technological know-how to combined heat and power technologies in order to derive highly efficient power from biomass and Biochar (charcoal derived as a by-product of the thermal conversion of biomass). This also serves to satisfy the earth's needs by compensating for the matter taken away over centuries of combusting coal, fossil fuel and natural gas.

Biochar is the key to stabilising world climate in the long term. The materials are stable against conversion by micro-organisms, whilst also optimising the soil composition of fields. This means that they not only serve as one means of achieving carbon dioxide mitigation but also prevent soil devastation. This is important because the stabilisation of world climate is the key to stabilising the water supply of countries like Canada, India, China and Switzerland, as well as continents like South America, all of which have a high percentage of glaciers.

Electric drive vehicles –
the need for brave decisions

Julia King

here seems to be a lot to be gloomy about at the moment. We are in the middle of a recession induced by excess – we have been encouraged to aspire to owning more and more things, bigger houses, bigger cars, and to take more and more distant holidays. Many in the developed world have come to enjoy and expect these luxuries, even though we cannot really afford them. The short-term meaning of 'we couldn't afford them' takes the form of the toxic loans packaged up in complex financial instruments which led to the banking crisis and now the recession. But we really cannot afford them in much more critical way than that. We cannot afford the carbon dioxide (CO_2) emissions.

Man-made CO_2 emissions (and those of other greenhouse gases) are driving up average global temperatures. There is now general agreement that the world must achieve at least a 50% reduction in CO_2 emissions (on 1990 levels) by 2050 if we are to avoid effects of climate change which will have a severe impact on human life. It is already unlikely that we will avoid a 2°C rise by the end of the century, bringing significant global challenges, especially for the poorest nations. Developed countries, like Europe and the US, need to reduce their emissions by at least 80% if all of the predicted 9 billion people on the earth in 2050 are to have an equal share of emissions. 'Equal shares' would mean that we would each be 'allowed' between 2 and 2.4 tonnes of CO_2 per year. That may sound a lot. But if you drive a car emitting 140 g/km of CO_2 (below the level of the European average new car in 2008) a distance of 15,000 km per annum (and many of us drive further than this), you emit 2.1 tonnes of CO_2 – your whole 2050 allowance used up in driving alone.

In developed countries, transport is the second largest emitter of CO_2, after power generation. In the UK, transport accounts for about 25% of annual emissions, but this rises to one-third of total emissions in the US. And emissions from transport continue to grow – the implementation of new technology is not keeping up with growth in use. Cars and vans are the main source of emissions – almost 70% of the CO_2 is emitted by transport in the UK.

Whilst the proportion of emissions associated with moving people and goods in developed countries is already very high, there will potentially be huge growth in the developing nations. There are around one billion vehicles in the world today. Dan Sperling and Deborah Gordon, in their recent book, *Two Billion Cars*, estimate that there will be two billion by 2020.

So if we are to maintain the levels of personal mobility which have supported our comfortable lifestyles and our economic prosperity, and to allow our neighbours in the less developed parts of the world access to the same benefits, we must reduce vehicle emissions dramatically and as a matter of urgency.

So why I am I optimistic? Because this is a really important and exciting challenge. It is a challenge that the UK has committed to, through the Climate Change Act 2008. It is a challenge that young people are interested in and that they want to contribute to. It is a challenge that is attracting people into science and engineering again. Delivering the solutions offers a platform to building the UK's advanced manufacturing base, providing interesting and creative new jobs. And in the area of transport, I think we can make low carbon cars a reality if we make the right decisions now. But it is urgent.

There are a number of options for reducing vehicle emissions: vehicle technology, fuel technology, consumer behaviour, information systems and modal shift can, and should, all make important contributions. But this scale of change is not going to be delivered by carbon-based fuels burnt in internal combustion engines, especially when the predicted growth in vehicle use worldwide is taken into account. The changes needed to achieve these reductions will be radical, and we need to make progress urgently – 2050 is only just over three 'car lifetimes' away.

Two potential approaches could reduce car emissions dramatically: electric (and plug-in hybrid) vehicles and hydrogen fuel cell vehicles. Both types are electric drive vehicles, with the electric power provided either by the battery or from hydrogen converted in a fuel cell. We must continue to develop both potential technologies, but the technology closest to application today is battery technology.

Battery technology is not yet as good as we would like it to be: we need smaller, more power dense and cheaper batteries, optimised for automotive applications. But battery technology is improving faster than many industry commentators thought would be possible just a year ago. And even today's batteries can offer fun, useful and clean cars, with ranges of 60–300 miles. However, they are still far too expensive.

Of the car journeys we make, 97% are less than 50 miles, accounting for 77% of the CO_2 emissions. A battery range of 50–100 miles would cover most of our needs – if you commute 30–50 miles to work each day an electric vehicle would be fine if you could charge it at work. A plug-in hybrid car with a 50-mile electric range could provide most of the benefits with extra assurance and flexibility.

People often say that there is no point in having an electric car and charging it on coal-fired electricity. This is not a valid argument – if you charge via the grid, you charge, effectively, on the average grid mix of generation. In the UK, the carbon intensity of our grid electricity is approximately 550g CO_2 per kW hour (kWhr). The efficiency of an electric vehicle, combined with this carbon intensity, means that the electric car would have 'effective emissions' at least 20% better than an equivalent petrol vehicle today.

Decarbonising our grid electricity is the most important thing we have to do in the UK to meet our carbon budgets. The report of the Committee on Climate Change indicates that the grid carbon intensity needs to be, and could be, reduced to 300g/kWhr by 2020 and 90g/kWhr by 2030 if we are to meet our CO_2 reduction targets. By 2030 the emissions for an electric vehicle would be around one-tenth of those of an equivalent petrol vehicle today – this target is a challenge, but it is not unachievable.

The extra power demand can be met. Indeed, as energy efficiency measures in other areas of the economy start to impact, from about 2012 onwards UK electricity consumption is predicted to fall. The area of most concern would be the local electricity distribution system, already under pressure from changing demands and the growth of local generation, so updating of electricity distribution will be essential, in any case, in the time period over which electric vehicles would be introduced.

If we are to achieve the major emissions reductions which we need, we have to accelerate technology development and take up of these radical automotive technologies. We need some brave decisions, both in government and in company boardrooms: focussing government support for research and development in key areas, funding for major demonstration activities and significant subsidies to encourage consumers to adopt new low emissions vehicle technologies and enable new business models.

We need to encourage existing and new players in the industry to see the UK as the place to be, where there will be support, interested and engaged consumers and the talent to take forward essential new developments. The challenge is big, but the opportunities it brings are exciting. I am optimistic that we can make a difference, for climate change and for the UK.

Plant evolution –
the key to a new generation

Juliet Coates

All the life on earth can be roughly divided into a few groups. Tiny bacteria, archaea (organisms a bit like bacteria) and viruses make up a huge portion of all living species. However, most of the living things that we actually see from day to day are part of a group of organisms known as the eukaryotes. Many eukaryotes are very familiar: all animals and plants fall into this category. Some are less generally familiar but none the less important: there are a plethora of single-celled eukaryotes that crawl or swim around. In this category we find both the plankton that fill and feed the oceans and many pathogenic species that infect animals and plants and cause disease.

The current belief is that all of these living organisms originated from a single ancestor formed when life on earth began about 3.5 billion years ago (give or take a few hundred million years). Some time between one and two billion years ago, a very important event occurred that shaped the existence of much of the life on earth that we see today. Somewhere in the primeval soup of unicellular organisms that existed at that time, a cell acquired a random mutation and hence a set of characteristics that enabled it to become the ancestor of all the plants that now exist. At around the same time, another cell was becoming the one that would give rise to all animal life.

We now have a pretty good idea of what the animal precursor cell was like; its relatives still exist, largely unchanged, in many aquatic environments today. Study of the fossil record played a large part in figuring out animal evolution, and more recently a better understanding of DNA has allowed our understanding to increase dramatically. Our knowledge of the evolution of plants, however, is more limited.

The transition of plants from water to land around 400 million years ago was a giant leap in plant evolution and allowed plants to colonise just about every square inch of the globe. It also led to a dramatic increase in the size and complexity of plants – think of giant redwood trees, which are pretty much the largest living things on the planet, and the complex and beautiful leafy and floral structures we enjoy in gardens and parks. In fact, most of the familiar, complex land-dwelling plants evolved in the last 200 million years or so.

But this still leaves a 'hole' of at least a billion years during which we have very little idea of what was going on in terms of plant evolution. Surely understanding how plants got to be the way they are remains one of the most seriously under-investigated areas of modern biology!

If we can trace the evolutionary history of the plants we see around us, we stand a better chance of being able to use them in a productive way. For example, by understanding how ancient plants made the journey to land, we can identify their drought-resistance strategies and manipulate modern plants to be more drought-resistant when required. In addition, algae are highly adaptable and can live in a huge variety of inhospitable environments – including in darkness! If we could encourage plants to use these algal mechanisms we could grow plants in many weird and wonderful places.

Over the last decade or two, scientific interest in plant biology has grown. The reasons for this are probably twofold. First, we eat plants. Pretty much everybody depends on one or more members of the grass family (rice, wheat etc) to provide their staple source of carbohydrate. Growing enough crops in the right places to sustain current world population growth is becoming increasingly challenging; we need to find ways to make plants grow in places that they would not normally be able to. The second reason is that many of the scientific tools that allowed us to understand a great deal about how bacteria, yeasts and animals work at the molecular level, including genetic engineering, can now be used to understand plant biology too.

One important breakthrough in recent years has been the ability to know the entire genetic composition of a particular organism. We can literally read all of the letters in an organism's DNA. This 'whole-genome sequencing' has transformed modern biology. We now know the whole-genome sequences of bacteria, yeasts, flies, worms, moulds, mice and humans, to name but a few. And comparison of the genomes of different organisms has allowed us to understand how complex animals evolved from that primeval eukaryotic soup.

The time is right to do the same for plants.

In the last decade, many plant genomes have been sequenced, including a number of important crop species and some plants that have not changed much in the last 400 million years, since they first appeared on land. This has provided some very important information about how plants evolved after their transition to land, but does not tell us how the original algal ancestor evolved over the previous billion or so years.

Twenty years ago the technology available meant that genome sequencing was a slow process: acquiring and processing a huge amount of data took years at a time. With new sequencing technologies and very, very fast computers, however, we can now sequence a genome in a week or two – and the study of plant evolution can make good use of this.

Very recently, for example, a few single-celled algal genomes were sequenced, providing some very interesting insights into the origins of plant life. There are so many different types of algae in so many different habitats that it is hard to get your head round them all. Some are simple; some are much more complex, being many-celled and having characteristics not completely unrelated to land plants. We now need to use the new technologies to sequence and analyse this massive diversity of algal genomes.

I predict that in the next decade this kind of analysis will enable our understanding of plant evolution to be as detailed and comprehensive as our current view of animal evolution. We will have filled a knowledge gap not addressed by Darwin, and I believe this will unlock the secrets of how all things green – from an aspidistra to a zinnia – came to be the way they are.

Urban ecosystems – tapping the human resource

Lucy Bastin

The past few decades have seen some incredible innovations in science, and some real progress in the social and political commitment needed to make high and low technology useful to real people in fair and sustainable ways. Despite these positive moves, it can at times be daunting to consider the prospects of the human race for living comfortably, or even tolerably, on the planet. Sometimes the inequalities and corruptions of the world make the big challenges of sustainable development seem overwhelming.

But when you look closer to home, at the level on which people experience and identify with their surroundings and their political institutions, there are many things to be positive about. This is where the motto 'Think Global – Act Local' starts to make sense, because in order to take an interest in environmental issues, people need an idea of what 'the environment' is, and to have access to something worth caring about.

Urban centres attract people at an ever-increasing rate. In the UK, around 90% of us already live in towns or cities. The Population Division of the UN estimates that by 2030, 4.9 billion people (around 60% of the world's population) will live in urban areas. In developed and developing countries alike, this puts considerable pressure on limited areas of land to create decent homes (or at least safe shelter), supply clean water and move large numbers of people around.

It is not surprising that, as urbanites, our experience of 'nature' is often biased towards majestic documentaries about spectacular environments that could (for all we know) no longer exist. Nor is it surprising that for many stretched cities, the immediate priorities of housing, industry and infrastructure eclipse longer-term landscape planning and 'luxuries' like green roofs, parks and gardens. The spaces where we gather are becoming more and more sterile and corporate (shopping malls are a good example of this).

However, most cities still have at least some open public space: parks, playgrounds and waterways, which are essential for encouraging physical activity and relaxation. Here in the West Midlands, the massive community support for the lottery-funded Black Country Living Landscape Programme, the success of the Forest Schools initiative and the growing popularity of allotments show that people from all walks of life appreciate these spaces, and are keenly interested in practical environmental activities. But without a vocal set of 'owners', public land can easily be lost. After all, allotments nationwide were sold off over the past 30 years, as interest temporarily waned, and are now in short supply.

In the UK, we have numerous legal and policy guidelines designed to protect natural areas and biodiversity, but all too often these are not sufficient to make a difference in practice, without pressure groups to act as guardians for areas under threat. I am confident that people everywhere can take on this role, identifying with urban green spaces and valuing the experiences they offer. Humans, after all, are not just consumers and polluters, they can be phenomenal resources. The persistence of grass roots movements such as housing and workers' co-operatives and land trusts and the fact that volunteering amongst young people in the UK is at its highest ever shows that, globally and nationally, there is a strong desire to take responsibility for managing and improving our surroundings.

I am also optimistic about the growing recognition that green spaces supply 'ecosystem services' which would otherwise cost money – that trees and vegetation can efficiently filter pollution, baffle sound, moderate 'heat island' effects and provide drainage which cushions us against flooding, as well as increasing the quality of life for urban residents. This sort of costing and valuation of the natural environment is an idea for which many respectable scientists have argued for decades, yet it is only just beginning to be taken seriously by governments and funding agencies.

Admittedly, this is not very holistic – it is a utilitarian approach which assumes that the natural world is there for us to use and manipulate – but these are tough and competitive times, and I believe we can and should use economic valuations as a policy tool to make our cities sustainable. In particular, when biodiversity is considered as an ecosystem service, it is not just rare and rural areas which have a role to play. Obviously, it is important to protect and preserve unique and special national parks, but we also need to face the fact that, globally, urban ecosystems are where most people will spend most of their time.

The UK is an excellent example – here, we actually have very few pristine environments, since as a small island the majority of our treasured 'natural' areas have historically been created, managed or modified by humans. Grazed downland, planted woods, moors and fishing lakes have all become rich environments for a huge range of plants and animals. In the same way, the gardens, canals, cemeteries and derelict land of cities can have great ecological value if managed well.

Urban areas have another huge resource which is undervalued and often effectively invisible – those scruffy little patches of derelict land. Biodiversity on urban brownfield sites is often surprisingly impressive, especially where insect species and their microhabitats are concerned. The disturbance which makes these sites look so unmanicured actually creates short-lived habitats which have become rare in city surroundings, and even in the countryside, now that industrial-scale farming, monocultures and pesticides are so prevalent. These areas, therefore, often form 'refugia' in which species can persist when they lose their habitat elsewhere.

This is illustrated by a 2004 survey of brownfield sites in the Eastside area of Birmingham by Donovan, Sadler and Bryson, which discovered numerous nationally and internationally scarce species of insects, 19 bird species identified by the International Union for Conservation of Nature as of conservation concern (including the black redstart) and two species of bat. Nor is this unusual – many studies of neglected urban sites from around the world find similarly rich and rare plant and animal communities.

It would be easy to be pessimistic about the future of these messy, scrappy areas and the species they support, as urban environments continue to be sanitised and developed. Unsurprisingly, brownfield sites have been prioritised for development and re-use in recent UK planning initiatives. In the Birmingham example above, the Eastside Biodiversity Strategy proposes many creative techniques for maintaining ecological value in the face of development pressure (including the replacement of lost brownfield areas with equivalent areas of 'brown roofs'). However, it also notes many missed opportunities and biodiversity losses in the development of the area so far.

But I think these places can and do matter to us. Most of the adults I have asked remember a secret den or outdoor place which, when they were young, they believed nobody else knew about. Often, these were unprepossessing little areas: land beside disused railways, pockets behind advertising hoardings – places we might avoid nowadays because they seem a bit risky. People recall observing spiders, ants, bugs, beetles, birds and even bats in these hideaways – it required patience and concentration then, and I do not actually believe that 'modern kids are incapable of concentrating'!

In fact, that is another thing I am encouraged by – people who you would think were incapable of slowing down often have incredible focus when it comes to exploring the natural world. Things happen slowly there, unpredictably and sometimes not at all. It is the opposite of the stimulating, game-like, bite-size style in which we now tend to approach education and recreation, but somehow it ends up being the opposite of boring. It makes me think that people of all ages – not just kids – are feeling the video deficit that stops us being completely satisfied with an indirect experience, and secretly want to spend some of their time experiencing the world hands-on. Unless we are genius abstract thinkers, it is usually how we learn best.

As you can tell from the yoghurt-weaving flavour of this article, the notion that we should value engagement with nature is pretty old-fashioned. However, these ideas seem to be perpetually valid, speaking to a lack that many people across the social spectrum are feeling, and fitting surprisingly well within the information society. Modern social and environmental activism and awareness is often mediated by, rather than replaced by, the internet.

Increasingly, many citizens are not being isolated by digital technology, but using it to co-ordinate real-world experiences, such as 'guerrilla gardening', organised nature walks and environmental flashmobs. And, in the UK, projects like OPAL (Open Air Labs) are co-ordinating scientists and people from all sorts of backgrounds to collaborate in exploring, studying and protecting their local environments. I think that is plenty to look forward to.

Urban nature reserves – partnership as stewardship

Veronica Lawrie

Our species has existed for over 200,000 years, thanks to an intuitive understanding of our environment and its value which has ensured our survival. In earlier times, living was more precarious and our connection with sources of water, food and shelter were a primary concern, but in more recent times, as our culture has become urbanised and industrialised, this vital connection to our basic life-giving resources has been forgotten.

As an ecologist, with a view of the interdependence of life and an understanding that all our wealth derives from our natural resources, you might wonder what I have to feel positive about. In fact, there are many exciting developments in the field of ecology: this science, of resource management, of the fragile and fertile web of life, is taking its place again in the decision-making process that takes us into our future.

Sir Nicholas Stern applied the idea of nature having an economic value and brought it to a global audience. In his 2006 *Review on the Economics of Climate Change*, he calculated that the cost of responding to climate change, which threatens the basic ecosystem services that support humans, would be greater the slower it was undertaken. By investing in a low carbon economy now, we would be able to minimise the financial costs associated with safeguarding clean water, food production and other ecosystem services.

The idea that a financial value could be placed on the environment establishes it as a national and global resource at a time when capitalist market forces drive societies. But in reality it has been difficult to assign a figure to a species, habitat or ecosystem service. For example, what is the financial value of crop pollination by bees? Is it the sum of the honey, vegetable and fruit market values? Without bees to pollinate our crops, Einstein predicted, and E O Wilson further explained, we will starve within four years.

International research projects are underway that chart the decline of species and the indicators of the health of ecosystems. The UN's *Millennium Ecosystem Assessment* is one such study, with input and review of over 1,300 authors from 95 countries. The World Wildlife Fund periodically publishes a *Living Planet Report* which includes a measure of trends in global vertebrate populations and society's average ecological footprint. This empirical approach enables us to understand natural life-support systems better. We will then be able to use our understanding to influence policy at an international level to protect and enhance our natural resources.

It is much easier to safeguard what we already have rather than try to recreate natural systems from scratch. For example, attempts have been made to recreate tropical forest on old mining tailings in Malaysia. Where gold and aluminium have been mined, large areas of spoil are created which hold very few nutrients. There is little or no soil structure to retain water, no shade to reduce evapotranspiration and desiccation and no soil seed bank. Eucalyptus saplings were one of the few species that could be reintroduced to these areas. Because they are not a native species, they are used as a 'nursery crop' to be removed in the long term. Gradually, the trees provide shade and microclimates for other pioneer species, and very slowly nutrients accumulate locally. For example, birds from the wider areas occasionally perch on the trees and drop seeds that had been eaten in nearby forest, thereby enriching the species diversity.

Unfortunately, studies to date have not succeeded in re-establishing primary rain forest on mining tailings – only a species-poor secondary forest has been created. In Borneo, however, where much of the primary forest is being converted to oil palm plantation, there have been successful attempts to return secondary forest to primary forest. Clearly, looking after ecosystems before they become too impoverished is the key to maintaining our natural resources: ecosystems and communities do not lend themselves to mechanical reductionism. Ecologists would explain their workings in terms of emergent properties, with the whole being greater than the sum of the interacting parts.

The international treaty that continues to play one of the most important roles for protecting UK wildlife – and indirectly ecosystem services – is the Convention on Biological Diversity, signed by the majority of the world's countries, including the UK, at the Rio Summit in 1992. This has led to new legislation protecting species and habitats, as well as to policy that prioritises conservation action for the most threatened species and habitats.

Wildlife policy is implemented through the Biodiversity Action Plan. It is within these legal and policy frameworks that ecologists give wildlife an agenda. The UK planning system is underpinned by international legislation and national policies which enable us to retain wildlife in the landscape as it develops with new infrastructure – towns and wind farms, for example. The system has its drawbacks, but it is a starting point from which we can learn and improve.

The power of collective effort is unquestionable. One collaborative project in the West Midlands I have recently been involved with is the development of a 50-year vision for Sutton Park National Nature Reserve. The vision includes ecological aspirations as well as social, economic and archaeological ones. To achieve consensus, we undertook a public consultation exercise of all stakeholder groups. To fulfil the 50 year vision, the site management plan was updated in light of the new goals, and I was able to draw on statutory and stakeholder priorities to contribute to the management plan with respect of biodiversity.

The site is the largest urban nature reserve, outside of a capital city, in Europe. It is an important resource in the region and draws over 2 million visitors each year. The park is rich in biodiversity and is an area of wilderness in an urban context, a green lung of the city and a reservoir of species and habitat that includes ancient woodland, heathland and mire, with a diverse assemblage of associated species, including invertebrate, avian and botanical species. A wide range of experts and stakeholders was consulted to ensure that the future of the park brings continuity as well as meeting the needs of the people who know and use it.

This partnership approach fosters stewardship of this resource. One of the key aims that came out of the consultation was for the park to be designated a UNESCO Biosphere Reserve, which would extend it, via a biodiversity enhancement area of similar habitats, to the heathlands of Cannock Chase Special Area of Conservation. This aspiration for the park will promote and demonstrate a balanced relationship between humans and the biosphere. These are exciting times to be an ecologist!

Sustainable drainage – from new age to next generation

Susanne Charlesworth

It may seem strange to start an article based on the premise of optimism with a reminder to some of horrific experiences of flooding and sewage in their homes, and to the more fortunate of us of watching scenes of devastation on the TV news. However, the summer floods in the UK during 2007 and 2008 brought home in some of the most devastating ways that the UK's aging sewerage infrastructure now simply cannot cope with the increasing demands made on it. Population increase is one problem, but there is also the spectre of climate change, bringing with it the prospect of higher temperatures, changing rainfall regimes, more storminess and flooding.

'Bigger pipes are not the solution to bigger storms' according to a 2008 report by Water UK. The report goes on to suggest that sustainable drainage

(SUDS) and 'sacrificial areas' are the ways forward – and I could not agree more. I set up a SUDS applied research group (SUDS ARG) at Coventry University three years ago and interest in this approach has rapidly increased in the intervening years. What started out as a rather left of field 'new age' technique is now being taken very seriously indeed.

SUDS is made up of a series of devices which can be used individually, or put together as a treatment 'train'. These devices either allow water to infiltrate or detain it; either way, they encourage the water to remain at source and to dissipate slowly. This is the complete opposite of traditional hard drainage in which water is constrained in conduits or pipes and removed from cities as soon and as fast as possible. The incorporation of SUDS into the cityscape therefore needs a philosophical change in the way that water is viewed. At present it is an embarrassment, buried, out of sight and out of mind, but it is time for a change in behaviour: people need to accept and allow for the behaviour of water.

SUDS devices include relatively 'hard' engineered porous paving systems (PPS). These allow water to infiltrate through them, or the PPS can be enclosed by a tanked system of geotextile to allow rainwater harvesting, or we can even incorporate ground source heat (GSH) slinky coils in their structure to provide multiple environmental benefits. An example of this is the Hanson Ecohouse on the Building Research Establishment site at Watford, UK, where we are monitoring the efficacy and efficiency of these combined approaches.

The 'softer' side of SUDS devices includes those which utilise vegetation such as green roofs, swales (linear depressions in the ground designed to receive runoff), ponds and wetlands. A good UK example of these, designed as a 'train', is at the Hopwood Motorway Service Area on the M42, where runoff from the car parks and lorry park is routed through a series of ponds before discharge to the Hopwood Stream.

SUDS can not only attenuate the storm peak, but in doing so will also deal with many contaminants, either dissolved in stormwater or carried on particulates suspended in the flow. Vegetated SUDS in particular offer amenity benefits for those living close to places such as ponds and wetlands, though they also allow biodiversity to flourish in urban areas not normally associated with a rich and diverse ecology.

The beauty of the SUDS approach is that it is multidisciplinary, embracing social sciences (eg what are people's attitudes to having a pond outside their front door serving as a flood defence and water treatment facility?) and geosciences (eg how much pollutant can a PPS retain?). What particularly excites me, however, is that SUDS can provide a flexible and efficient means of both mitigating and adapting to climate change. In fact, I am convinced that SUDS will prove to be an essential weapon in the arsenal against climate change in the future.

Water in SUDS devices has been described as a 'liquid asset', and there are many ways in which SUDS can tackle the impacts of climate change whilst also lowering the urban heat island effect. These include carbon sequestration, greening and cooling urban areas, reducing energy usage and reducing the wind tunnelling effects of built-up areas.

Any SUDS device utilising vegetation or open water such as ponds will absorb carbon to a certain extent, and the value of this becomes obvious when you consider that in one year the average family car can produce up to one tonne of carbon. There are very few studies of this, but the Los Angeles Environmental Affairs Department quotes an area of prairie grass which sequestered 700 tonnes of carbon in 2000.

Green walls and roofs also act as insulators, keeping buildings cool in summer, reducing air conditioning use, and warm in winter, reducing heating costs. In 2008, for example, the Greater London Authority reported that an 850 square metre retrofitted green roof on a building in Canary Wharf saved an estimated £4,000 to £5,000 a year in electricity costs.

Cities are generally a few degrees warmer than the surrounding countryside. This is called the urban heat island effect and is due to the materials making up urban areas absorbing heat during the day and releasing it at night. Rural areas are cooler because vegetation has a cooling effect, partly because of the shade it provides but also due to the process of evapotranspiration occurring in its leaves, which cools the overlying air.

Vegetated SUDS devices such as green roofs and walls will cool urban areas in the same way, as will the planting of more street trees. Hard SUDS such as PPS which store water in their structures evaporate this into the overlying atmosphere and this too can add considerably to the cooling effect. Ponds and wetlands also make significant heat sinks. In fact, if every large city in the world used SUDS, this could make significant inroads to reducing global temperature.

Whilst the 2007 and 2008 floods were disastrous, they have brought alternative approaches to drainage to the fore. Traditional approaches are no longer sustainable and do not provide the multiple benefits that SUDS bring. These include water quality improvements, increased biodiversity opportunities, amenity and aesthetics and finally – and most importantly – a powerful weapon in the armoury against climate change.

In the future, I see cities as blue and green rather than grey and brown. I see them as attractive and pleasant places to live, cool and clean and in a fit state to hand on to future generations. I see SUDS playing a major role and water becoming an integral and valued part of our lives – as it ought to be.

CHAPTER 4

Living in the virtual world

Human computer interaction – making our lives better

Russell Beale

In an age when cynicism is rife, when it is easier and safer to criticise and be negative, to be asked, as a scientist, what things give cause for cheerfulness and a positive perspective on the future is an interesting question. For me, the answer to the question is relatively straightforward: it is the transformative power of technology that is now accessible to almost everyone. But not the technology itself. Let me explain.

I am a computer scientist, studying human-computer interaction (known by its acronym, as are many things in computing, HCI). HCI is the study of how people and digital technologies interact with each other, and so HCI people need to know a little about a lot of things – psychology, social science, technology, programming, design, evaluation and so on. HCI tends to be technology-neutral, looking at all aspects of digital media and interaction, with a focus predominantly on identifying and supporting user needs (current and future), with theoretical, scientific and applied aspects all featuring as appropriate. Put it another way: I play with and design fun gadgets and computer programs that make people's lives better in some way.

A few examples will illustrate my perspective. I have recently been on holiday in France, and we met up with a friend who lives out there. Whilst we were staying with him, his father was taken ill and he needed to get back to Scotland in a hurry. Within 15 minutes of receiving the phone call in the evening, he was booked onto a train that would take him to Paris, where he would take a flight to Edinburgh and be there the next day. All this was done via the internet, and in that time he had been able to identify four different routes to get back, see which would be fastest, check the costs, book the seats, pay for the selected route and receive his tickets. Such power and flexibility was unknown even a decade ago.

Mobile phones in Africa provide a very different illustration of the contribution technology can make to our world. Some entrepreneurs, for example, travel for days into the city to bulk-buy pre-paid mobile phone cards, and then travel back into rural communities and offer them for sale. The small revenues they make can serve to lift them and their families out of desperation and into education. Other enterprising approaches are used, too: in one rural area, I know of a man who makes money by spending almost all he has on a weekly football magazine, then charging people a small fee to text them the latest scores and news.

This sort of enterprise is only possible through the mobile phone, which provides connectivity and hence a route for commerce that would otherwise not be possible. Mobile phones are the computer for the developing world – they are relatively cheap, light, tough, can be solar powered, have (in general) acceptable connectivity and are powerful enough to perform basic computation and run simple programs.

One of my research projects looks at how we are using social networking systems at the moment, and how we may want to use them in the future. We have developed a mobile application that tracks your position, and shares it with your friends via your social network, allowing you to see who is around you and available to meet for a coffee, or dinner, or to come to a research seminar or whatever. One of the things that we have found is that for these systems to be acceptable to people, we have to give them some control over how their location is shared, in order to protect their privacy. Interestingly, we have found that people often lie about their location, even to their close friends, and, even more interestingly, the more they use social networking technologies, the more likely they are to lie. This could be because they want to retain some control and privacy about where they are, as a counterbalance to sharing much of the rest of their everyday activities – or it could be that they are more engaged in arranging surprise parties, shopping for presents for loved ones or similar – we have not yet determined which reasons are more prevalent.

My point in these examples is that it is not the technology that I am optimistic about – technologies come and go. It is not the internet that I think is wonderful, or computers, social networking or mobile phones. It is the fact that such systems are now available to most people, that they are understood by people, that people manage to use them reasonably well and that people can use them to do the things that they want to do with them. It allows individuals to work collectively and have a stronger voice; it puts communication, networking, social contact, political power, economic change, entertainment, education, access to information and advice – essentially, opportunity – into the hands of practically everyone.

This inspires me, because by empowering and supporting people, we can flourish as individuals, develop as families, grow as communities and support each other as citizens. And that has to be a cause for optimism.

Computer games – window to another world

Stuart Slater

omputer games engage users of all ages by suspending their disbelief. These games provide a portal to fantastic worlds where dragons and aliens inhabit locations rich in fantastic fauna and strangely designed buildings which users are free to explore and solve puzzles. This window to another world allows the imagination to be put on hold whilst the user experiences the designer's imagination instead, a novel experience that engages emotional and cognitive capabilities in unexpected situations – for example, where zombies populate a planet and survival depends on online co-operation with players in distant countries.

Of course, these games are often played to break the tedium of our everyday lives, allowing us to forget briefly the seriousness of political and social change; instead, exercising our minds with puzzles, or simply letting them wander and our senses be bombarded with fantasy settings. And technological advances in gaming are providing new interaction options, such as motion control sensors and video capture devices. These are capable of putting the player into the middle of fantasy worlds, providing a more immersive experience.

Some advances are in the area of intelligent characters or even characters that exhibit human-like emotions. My own collaborative research with Daden Ltd, for example, has led to advances in emotionally responsive characters in virtual worlds. These characters can be programmed to be afraid of snakes or happy to see their favourite pet, some can get angry when provoked in conversation and others simply have moods which dissipate over time.

These game technologies are growing in popularity and helping to fuel interest and sales of video games, whilst the target market is being broadened to include parents as well as children, positioning them as an integral part of family life. Some consoles and games can help to bring together families to engage in activities such as creating new interactive worlds, playing their favourite sports and even choosing a new virtual online presence that they can use in each of their games. Each family member can now have their own unique video game character that other players recognise them by, and which can be used to track game play experience or fitness levels.

With careful design and development, these games can also be used to educate the user in subject areas that are difficult or simply too boring to teach in a classroom. That is why some school management teams which have identified student preoccupation with video games have approached researchers for help in designing video games to help teach maths and history. In one example, volunteer students who were interested in gaming were recruited at the Shelfield Community Academy to work on games for use by fellow students. The recruits were selected because they were interested in developing game content and educational game ideas. Through the support of their school and in collaboration with a local university, they were given the opportunity to work with game developers and leading video game researchers to use commercial tools to help develop educational games.

This perked-up interest of the younger generation is not an isolated example: in fact, an ever-growing number of younger students are asking how these games are created and how they can learn to make them. Some students draw their favourite characters and later dream up their own creations that they will put down on paper or digitally, which may lead them to become a new generation of game artists; others use the additional game content to alter their world, changing both the look and behaviour of the game. These students may well become the next generation of programmers and developers.

Whichever path these youngsters take, the important consideration is that they are both engaging with the content and drawing on these new worlds to fuel their creativity and feed their imagination. What is certain is that many of these children will learn invaluable skills that might mean not only that their maths and science skills improve, but also that programming skills appear at an earlier age. Others may later decide that the games they used to play are not where their careers lie, but they may nevertheless join a new generation of engineers and designers whose previously fuelled imagination and creativity will help them shape the world of tomorrow.

Near field communications – re-imagining the mobile phone

Garry Homer

R adio-frequency identification (RFID) technology has been around since the end of the Second World War. However, whilst it has been adopted by large corporate companies such as Marks and Spencer, it has never quite taken off in the mass market. Some of the reasons for this are the cost of the hardware, immature and evolving standards and the bad press linked to privacy that has surrounded the topic for so long.

Near field communications (NFC) technology is a branch of RFID that could gain RFID the exposure and adoption that has long been promised. It has the potential to be deployed in many types of application and has considerable benefits for the target audience, including significant benefits to the individual that could go some way to redressing the current negative image.

NFC is a short-range high frequency wireless communication device; its main objective is the exchange of data over a short distance (maximum five centimetres). It is currently being deployed into mobile phones and the distinct advantage of this technology over similar hardware is that the mobile phone can act as both as a tag and as a reader. It is an extension of the existing ISO/IEC 1443 proximity card standard, which means as well as being compatible with other NFC phones it can be used with other contactless hardware.

What does this mean for the consumer? One of the key drivers of NFC applications is the release in late 2009 of a mobile phone with NFC integration on the SIM card (Nokia 6216), which will enable operators to build NFC services onto the SIM card. This will enable payment and ticketing transactions to be carried out with a quick swipe of the phone. The existing features of NFC include ease of data and image exchange and there is the potential for the technology to expand at a rapid rate.

NFC has many potential uses, which include systems for the visually impaired, the deaf and others who might benefit from assisted living. An example is a system that has been developed to help the elderly and people with Alzheimer's-type problems to call for assistance in an emergency. The system works by allowing the placing of NFC tags in pictures of the patient's relatives or the emergency services. When the patient needs to make an emergency call, they simply swipe the phone over the picture of their relative and a phone call or text message is sent instantly – there is no need for the person to remember or look up telephone numbers.

One of the many advantages of NFC technology is that it will seamlessly and simply integrate into our everyday lives, adding benefit and bringing improvements in the quality of life. In the future you will be able to place your debit card on to the SIM of your mobile phone and simply swipe for payments, reducing the number of debit cards you need to carry around. Because of these benefits and the ease of integration, NFC is expected to be used worldwide by consumers.

Another use of the technology is in the 'intelligent poster', a way of including considerable added-value information in standard, low-cost (paper) posters. One of the biggest advantages here is the ability to stream real time information to the user. For example, with the integration of NFC tags, users can be prompted to buy tickets for a forthcoming film when they are viewing the poster, regardless of their current location. In addition, the dynamic nature of the intelligent, NFC-enabled poster allows not only ticket prices but also up-to-the-minute specific seat availability to be displayed, as well as other relevant details such as travel timetables.

A similar short range communications platform to NFC is Bluetooth. This technology has been around for some time and may have a better data transfer rate and a larger coverage area, but it cannot target specific host devices: it simply covers an area with its transfer and all compatible devices in the zone will communicate. NFC is aimed at data transfer at a much shorter distance. There are other differences which separate the two technologies into unique standards, but when they are integrated they complement each other and provide a myriad of possibilities.

Another advantage of this technology is that the NFC reader module can be used to pair two phones. This bypasses the existing, cumbersome pairing process of the Bluetooth standard. When the phones are in the vicinity of each other (around 2 cm), they are prompted to pair, the exchange/handshake takes place with minimal user input and then the phones are ready for data transfer.

The University of Wolverhampton's 'IT Futures Centre' has collaborated with a number of companies in the four years it has been in existence. A growing number are evaluating RFID and NFC technologies with the possibility of integrating these into the processes, products and services that they sell to their customers.

One of the most recent projects involves integrating NFC into an application to aid visually impaired people in navigating their way around unfamiliar buildings. The application centres on the placement of NFC tags at specific locations from where the users can be instructed by guidance information provided in verbal and/or visual formats. The beauty of integrating an application into a device like a mobile phone is that it is an everyday device and people are familiar with its usage. This means that the learning curve is drastically reduced when compared with employing a new, dedicated device. And because a mobile phone is capable of streaming images and audio, the user only needs one device – not a whole pocketful.

In the light of all these advantages, it is not surprising that Håkan Djuphammar, Ericsson's VP of systems architecture, has already predicted that by the summer of 2010 NFC technology will be in all new mobile phones, paving the way for the rapid expansion of NFC-enabled applications. The world of the mobile phone user is about to be transformed!

Object-based media – quantum information

Jeremy Foss

Attitudes to extending personal information into the internet (aka 'the cloud') are notoriously generational: mature patrons (the ones with mortgages, responsibilities and experience) are rightly guarded and suspicious. Adventurous teen and early twenties are all too keen to tweet, poke and share their inner – and outermost – feelings and activities with the internet (and therefore the world) in a highly cavalier manner. However, betraying your character to the internet may soon become much more insidious … and possibly rewarding.

Telecommunications service operators are investing heavily in internet protocol television (IPTV) as part of the voice, video and data triple play service bouquet. The three services are converging into a lucrative integrated platform for commercial interactivity. Cable TV companies are similarly looking to converged IPTV/data to gain a similar commercial advantage, and the largest investment within global IPTV is targeted advertising. However, the next generation of video services will likely be using object-based media. As Al Jolson said at the birth of multimedia: 'You ain't heard nothin' yet.'

Object-based media will extend user interaction right into the contents of the TV stream. The overt manifestation of this is the ability for users to click objects within the programme scenes to utilise interactive services which are embedded in the content, or link through to an external web service. The covert side of this is the correlation and assimilation of these interactions on a global scale. There is also the capability for the placement of objects and items into the programme (audio or video) relating to an individual's profile.

Personalised advertising is an obvious objective here, and whilst this may be seen as stealth, it has benefits. More obvious beneficial applications include cultural customisation of content, educational and training applications and even pure personalised entertainment. However, the suspicions are easy to envisage: would certain user/media interactions reduce chances of employment or insurance ... or could they invoke an interactive teaching programme for the viewer? If it is commercial (and most services are), it depends where the money is. However, education, health and other public authority services could also allow users to benefit greatly from this degree of personalised media.

Of course, ever since the introduction of the loyalty card, customers have been subjected to high scrutiny on a very detailed scale. Armies of statisticians manage the systems which correlate the data of millions of shoppers and other online users for the plethora of info-trails they generate. Stephen Baker calls these statisticians the 'Numerati' in his book of that name.

Data protection legislation around the world takes different approaches to separating personal identity from the behavioural patterns, but this anonymity is fragile. We currently yield certain preferences into the internet via basic grocery lists, innocuous entries in social networking sites, transactions on a retailer site, credit card trails etc. Assessment of user behaviour based on this rough granularity of information is effective but still fairly vague and it often leads to the puzzling marketing data we receive in return.

This process is akin to conventional Newtonian mechanics: tangible discrete forces of user information. However, interactivity and more efficient interfaces are encouraging us to betray more of our behaviour and preferences in incredibly fine detail. Information correlation and assimilation across the nascent semantic web interrogates down to the microscopic detail of an online user's character, with the assumption that the real-world person is fairly similar.

We could call this 'quantum information' – tightly defined quanta of metadata which have a completely different mechanics to the simplistic evaluation of a loyalty card. It operates with the smallest fragments of information groomed from the global information bases which have accrued from our relationships with service providers, and also with each other. This means that rather than just generating a user profile, internet-based services recognise us by a contextual character which changes depending on situations, in the same way as humans recognise character traits in other people.

Consequently, media projected to us will become increasingly personalised, ostensibly for entertainment. This also means that advertising becomes not only targeted but also highly personalised. Whilst this could initially be disquieting, it could be highly relevant and informative. It also eliminates junk content, since service providers and their agencies can narrowcast to individuals, rather than using the wasteful speculative spread-shot approach. In any case, advertising in its current form is drifting towards extinction and needs a more intelligent approach which not only informs but satisfies all its clients on a higher intellectual and personal level.

Virtual worlds are certain to play an increasing role in our lives and are now emerging with more serious intent than the initial primitive 3D social networking playgrounds for disembodied avatars. When interactive TV converges with virtual worlds, an interesting mix of capabilities will tip the balance towards the provision of highly compelling serious applications for education, training and design visualisation. Whilst this may not entirely substitute for hands-on experience, it does extend near-practical education to remote and disparate groupings of users. Distance and travel becomes less of a problem; there are obvious environmental benefits and this allows more effective personal time management. With real estate less of an issue in virtual environments, cultural mixing and appreciation may be more easily achieved and diversity is a potentially huge beneficiary.

So there are reasons to be optimistic, but also to be cautious. The more use we make of the internet's knowledge of ourselves, the better. However, we also want clever tools acting for us which manage the data flow across the human-internet boundary, ie an intuitive secretary. As always, the technology on both sides of the fence will result in cat-and-mouse iterative advances in intrusion, detection and prevention technologies for both end-user and service provider.

The future internet is an internet that knows you better than you know yourself. Further down the road we will see the internet working increasingly close to the human cognitive interfaces, in effect a cyborg-net: billions of humans plus the internet equals a technology-genomic hybrid where the internet aggregates, processes and utilises our collective intelligence and knowledge. It may already be beyond the bounds of legislation and morality as to whether this is a benefit or a threat – so be on your guard. But I am confident that there is much to gain from the future internet both personally and globally.

Human-machine interface – full-body motion control

Vinesh Raja

The user interface, also known as human-computer interface (HCI) or man-machine interface (MMI), is the means by which humans (users) interact with the system, namely a particular machine, device, computer program or other complex tool. The users are interacting with machines that are essentially fairly dumb in terms of communications.

Since the advent of the computer, computers have become more powerful, monitors have become slimmer and the keyboard and mouse have become wireless, but fundamentally the interface remains unchanged. This has imposed on humans a requirement to adapt their habits, behaviour and mindset to the technology. We have improved our productivity by using the tools and devices designed especially for daily tasks. But we have also constrained our natural abilities to the features of the very tools and devices that we have become dependent on.

We have got used to a number of things, from the traditional keyboard and mouse-based user interfaces, to 2D Windows-based user interface and to a rather unspectacular user's workflow which enables typically one user to interact with only one application at a time. At present most of us are stuck with Windows, icons, keyboard and mouse.

Good user interfaces are crucial for good user experiences. It does not matter how good a technology is, if the user interface is not intuitive and attractive, the technology will not break into the market. To gain user interest and engagement in a new product or technology, the user interface needs to be intuitive and adaptive – intuitive so that no specific training is needed and adaptive so that the user interface can be personalised.

Today, most mobile phone users tend to change their phones typically at least once every two years. Most users customise various functions on their mobiles based on their daily needs. When users change their phones, they have to learn the new user interface and new features, and transfer data from their old mobile to the new one. In this scenario, the users are constantly adapting to technologies.

I am confident that this will soon be a thing of the past. Future mobile phones will not only talk with the old ones and transfer the data but will also customise certain functions based on knowledge of what features the owner used on their old phone. This is what I call an intelligent technology: one that understands its users and configures itself to meet their needs. For example, in the near future mobile phones will be using diary information, location technology etc to determine whether the phone should be automatically switched to silent.

Humans naturally use speech, gestures and 3D interactions with touch (haptics), smell and taste capabilities to interact with the real environment. I believe that we will encounter combinations of some of these modes of interaction in the not too distant future. Haptics at present is being targeted for the games industry but is also playing a major role in healthcare applications such as virtual surgery and stroke rehabilitation.

Multi-touch devices accept input from multiple fingers and multiple users simultaneously, allowing for complex gestures, including grabbing, stretching, swivelling and sliding virtual objects across the table. Whilst touch sensing is commonplace for single points of contact, multi-touch sensing enables a user to interact with a system with more than one finger at a time, as in chording and bi-manual operations. Such sensing devices are inherently also able to accommodate multiple users simultaneously, which is especially useful for interactive walls and tabletops.

Multi-touch is already widely used. For example, Apple's iPhone has multi-touch scrolling and picture manipulation, whilst Microsoft's interactive surface utilises multi-touch technology and allows a user or multiple users to manipulate digital content by the use of natural hand gestures or by putting physical objects on the surface.

Other applications will open up new worlds of interaction.

Cybersphere, for example, is the world's first fully 3D immersive virtual environment. The Cybersphere is a translucent acrylic sphere 3.5 m in diameter, weighing 280 kg and floating on cushion of air. Up to eight projectors mounted around the Cybersphere immerse the user in a fully immersive 3D virtual environment and it utilises the user's natural walking as an interface for navigating through virtual spaces.

In a similar vein, Microsoft's project Natal is a motion-sensing device that allows you to control video games and Xbox 360 menus with your body instead of a peripheral controller. Natal gives you voice and full-body motion control over your onscreen avatar using an RGB camera, depth sensor, multi-array microphone, and custom processor running proprietary software.

Finally, Extreme Reality (XTR) is a world leader in 3D human-machine interaction. XTR introduces a patented technology of 3D human-machine interface (3D HMI) which allows users to operate digital devices, play games and interact in virtual worlds using natural human hand and body motions. XTR technology delivers a real time, software-based, full-body 3D motion capture engine, using a single standard webcam, without any additional accessories.

Advances of this kind are not limited to our social and ludic worlds. The IWARD project, for example, uses touch screen and voice-based interface for hospital nurses to communicate with service robots for various healthcare scenarios such as delivery, guidance, cleaning etc.

So how will future user interfaces look? I believe they will be more human friendly, highly intuitive, intelligent (understanding their user's needs) and adaptive.

The digital world – design by humans, coding by computers

Kathleen Maitland

Ask many young people about the future and most of the time you will receive a negative response. If you ask them about 'Science' a common response will be 'it's boring', 'it's too difficult'. In my field of computing, I find that many young people don't want to do programming. Why? 'It's boring', 'it's too difficult'.

As a computer specialist I marvel at the computer games people play, and it is not just kids and teenagers who play these games. Have you noticed the dexterity required to handle games controllers? Have you seen how quickly and skilfully the players have to react to three-dimensional images presented on a two-dimensional screen?

Games can be anything from playing a guitar or drums, or even conducting an orchestra. You can surf, ski, fly jets, drive cars, fight or play war games. Games controllers can be anything from joysticks, steering wheels and pedals, tennis rackets, golf clubs, guitars, drums – the list appears to be endless. And, of course, there is what we now consider a standard games controller with its two crosses. Who said computing was boring!

Teams of systems developers design and write the complex computer programs that run the games. From the tennis programs of the 1980s to the world of the Sims, flight simulators, to the racing games of the Grand Turismo programs, the complexity and seeming reality into which the games draw the players has increased year on year. We have seen innovative systems such as the Wii, with its controller and nunchuck add-on, and the very popular Wii Fit Balance board pushes forward how we interact with games and games consoles.

Complex computer systems, like those found in games machines, require complex computer programs. These have to be designed and implemented. Since the 1960s, developers of computer programs have adopted the 'systems' way of thinking, in contrast to developing programs through a functional perspective using flow charts. But as the world of computers expanded, the complexity of computer programs increased – and the way computer programs were developed had to change to meet this challenge. Techniques that were developed to design computer programs which translated into thousands of lines of code were not robust enough to design programs of millions of lines of code. Programs could no longer be designed by one person; complex designs had to be communicated to programmers, and validated by non-computer specialists; programs could no longer be written by one person but demanded teams of programmers. Developing some computer programs in itself became a complex process.

A change was required to enable developers to think about the requirements of a complex computer system – just thinking about the required functionality was complex in itself. Models and techniques were developed to enable developers to understand what was required before they coded designs into software, and methodologies were created that stated which techniques should be performed and when. The development of complex computers and their associated programs has become more and more complex and more and more difficult to understand.

The change from designing systems from the required functionality to that of systems thinking required a change in the way developers think. Initially, the concept of systems thinking was introduced to enable developers to obtain an holistic view of a complex computer program under development. In the early days it could be difficult to obtain a systems view from reviewing all the models which had been created – the concept of systems thinking can be easily lost in a plethora of models.

As decades passed, more and more systems development methodologies were created, but today the most popular ones are based on unified modeling language (UML). This language is complex in itself, having precise syntax and notation, and the number of models of computer systems associated with it is continually increasing.

This brief history of how computer programs were developed highlights how complex the process of systems development has become. What has been lost in the vast number of models constructed and methodologies created is the ability to take an holistic view of a computer system and the environment it operates in.

This is where I believe the world of gaming that enthrals the children and young people of today will lead to the discovery of a simpler way of developing and coding complex programs. Their world is digitally enabled and powered by computers. They may not look at the world through system thinking, but they do look at the world through computer systems. They have the potential to think differently and discover a way of providing an holistic view of a computer system using computer systems and complex software in a similar way to the way they play computer games, supported by controls different from the keyboard and mouse we use today.

As a discipline, we need a jump in knowledge to provide a better way of constructing computer programs which will meet the needs of organisations, but knowledge pertaining to software architecture that is flexible and agile enough to accommodate change. There is a need for a new way of thinking. As we look to the future, where will the next jump in the knowledge of building computer systems come from?

The world in which we and our children play, explore, discover and create information has changed. I have observed an increase in dexterity, and response to events and stimuli. I have listened to a change in language which now includes text speak, but also includes Latin and Greek creeping back in through games programs. When I was a child, you would never hear children talking about metaphorisms or transpositions, or discussing appropriate strategies to win a game. I regularly hear children as young as ten years old use these terms correctly today. I do not think I would have known what the term 'strategy' meant, let alone use the word. And as for concepts like avatars, which my young son enjoys drawing, then creating on his computer …

We are observing the evolution of the digital world, run by computer programs – design by humans and coding by computers.

The world has changed, and computers are ubiquitous. Whilst many young people are not optimistic about their future and the world they live in, there is so much for them to be optimistic about. The world of science and technology has advanced so much. The Large Hedron Collider brought science back onto TVs and radio, where the digital age lets us view, record and replay programmes. Computers provide access to the internet, where gigabits of information are available at the touch of a keyboard. Social networks enable people from all around the world to interact. Science is pushing the boundaries ever forward and computers are there, supporting, processing, displaying and constructing information by running programs on a variety of platforms.

We live in a world that I could not have dreamed of as a child. There is the potential for today's children to think differently as they live in a digitally enabled world. Today, I see young people with higher dexterity and faster reactions accepting change, drawing from the past and thinking differently – and who knows what breakthroughs they will make in the future. I expect it will be outside my concepts and imagination. I am optimistic that the vast potential that young people have in the way that they think and the way that they interact with technology will lead to scientific breakthroughs which we could never dream of.

Virtual worlds – Turing-capable chatbots

David Burden

n 1950, the British computer scientist Alan Turing described what he called the 'imitation game', which has since become the most well-known test of computer, or artificial, intelligence. In essence, the test is about whether a human having a conversation with another entity through a computer terminal can tell whether that correspondent is a human or a computer.

Many, myself included, doubt whether the Turing Test is actually a good (or even sufficient) test of artificial intelligence – assuming by artificial intelligence (AI) we mean a computer that can think, learn and act for itself (and just the definition of those words in an AI context is the subject of much debate). But the Turing Test does offer a good test of what is called chatbot technology –

computer programs designed to mimic human conversation, but with no claims to being intelligent.

Most people are familiar with chatbots through web-based customer service agents such as Ask Anna on the IKEA web site. You ask them a question in plain English and hopefully they give you a useful (or at least sensible) answer back. Even this though, beyond a very narrow subject domain, is actually a very hard thing to do. Since 1990, the American Hugh Loebner has run the Loebner Prize – an annual chatbot competition modelled on the Turing Test. For many this has been the most visible sign of progress, or lack of progress, towards the Turing Test. Indeed, if you look at this sample exchange from the 2009 competition it can sometimes be hard to tell whether even the judge is human, let alone the computer!

'Local:	Yes, you know, how are things?
Remote:	Are you still convinced I'm the computer and you're not?
Local:	There's no question of me being a computer, it's you or the kid.
Remote:	Yes there was a question mark.
Local:	Not sure what you mean about the question mark, can you explain?
Remote:	I was merely answering you question, which unfortunately did not use proper punctuation, yet again.
Local:	Ok, how are you?
Remote:	You don't seem to make much sense. I asked you a question and you froze, why?
Local:	I'll answer the question: you are the computer, I am not.
Remote:	I am God.
Local:	Is that a delusion? Do you need help?
Remote:	I am what I am, predictability is simply a mental construct designed to understand the world. I am above that, I do not play by your rules.'

The big problem with the Loebner Prize is that both judges and confederates (the humans talking to the judges) know that they are taking part in a Turing Test. So the judges tend to ask convoluted questions that no person would ever ask in real life, and the confederates appear to delight in trying to tease the judges into thinking that they are in fact the computer.

In conditions like this it is not surprising that little progress appears to be being made.

Were such a state of affairs to continue, then I think people would be rightly pessimistic about whether we would ever pass the Turing Test (Turing himself thought it would be passed 30% of the time by 2000), but I for one am optimistic that we will see a Turing Test passed within the next few decades, maybe even within a single decade.

In developing AIs there are a number of schools of thought. At the most 'organic' are those who believe that an AI could be built from the ground up using exact analogs of how the brain works – for example, through vast numbers of digital neurons. At the next level of abstraction are 'neural nets', computer programs that mimic the behaviour of networks of neurons without exactly replicating the behaviour of individual neurons. This technology has worked well in areas like image processing and classification – but appears to have little to offer a chat-based bot. Others (such as Ray Kurzweil in *The Singularity is Near*) simply claim that as computer power reaches the equivalent of the human brain 'intelligence' will somehow spontaneously emerge.

My view is that we will pass the Turing Test soon, but by none of these methods. My optimism is based on two developments. The most important change in information technology in the last decade has been the emergence of the world wide web (and the services and technologies that it has spawned). In the next decade I expect that virtual worlds technologies will become just as important. Together these are, I believe, key to the development not only of a successful chatbot program, but possibly to the development of a true AI.

The web is important for three reasons. First, through web services and the information on it, the web provides us with easy ways to answer a whole variety of 'fact'-type questions. For instance, if we want a bot to answer the question 'Who wrote *The Stone Diaries*?' we just get the bot to recognise the pattern 'who wrote …' and then fire the rest of the sentence to Amazon's web service to get the author of *The Stone Diaries*. Of course, this will fail sometimes – but it is a great improvement over having to code every fact by hand!

Secondly, the web holds a vast amount of 'chat', much of it indexed, and some available in real time through services such as Twitter. This can not only provide an ideal corpus for programmers looking to emulate human chat, but can also be mined dynamically to find responses to many questions or statements and to introduce more 'human' responses. Thirdly, a wide variety of novel programming and data management models have emerged from the web, such as topic maps and the semantic web, which we can easily leverage in the building of better chatbots and AIs.

Whilst the internet might provide the 'hard' ingredients in the creation of a good chatbot, virtual worlds (such as Second Life) can provide the 'soft' elements that are so often lacking in chatbot and AI development. In a virtual world a computer-driven avatar looks no different from a human-driven avatar (although neither need look human, or indeed robotic). The computer also 'sees' as much information about the world as the human does, and can interact with it to exactly the same extent. In a virtual world we have a level playing field for any twenty-first century Turing Test. Indeed, what excites me is the fact that we can develop more modern implementations of the Turing Test which perhaps offer a far fairer test than the Loebner Prize. Two are of particular interest.

One we call the covert Turing. It is trivial to place a chatbot-driven avatar in a virtual world like Second Life and see how human-driven avatars respond to it. If those humans have a five-minute conversation with the bot and do not twig that the avatar is indeed a bot then have we passed the Turing Test? Another variation is the Group Turing, where we place a chatbot-driven avatar in a large group of people – like a cocktail party. In such an environment the bot actually does not have to talk much to seem human – just to say 'yes' and 'hmm' at appropriate points! In both cases the game has changed subtly, but significantly, from the bot having to *prove* it is a human to just having not to *give away* the fact that it is not. There are, of course, ethical issues in such tests which need to be addressed as well.

In a virtual world it is important, though, that the bot masters more than just chatting – so in some ways the bar is higher than for the traditional teletype-based Turing Test. Any chat in a virtual world is likely to include comments about the surroundings, and the avatars are likely to move around – so the bot must have some degree of spatial awareness. Also the bot now has a full range of body gestures and even facial expressions at its disposal, and so it needs to deploy these correctly to support what it is saying, and in its reactions to what it hears and sees. Actually, the problem in many virtual worlds is that it is easier for the bot to trigger gestures and expressions than it is for humans – so the bots 'seem' more human (even too human) to the external observer from the start. One criticism, though, of the use of virtual worlds for a Turing Test is that they give the bot more scope to 'cheat' – using its looks and gestures to distract from the content of the chat – but is not that actually more like real life?

The real opportunity of virtual worlds is that they give the bot an environment in which to live and even grow. The growth in human intelligence is often attributed to our need to cope with and respond to changes in our environment. We only 'know' things like colours and emotions and chairs and tables because we use them, share them or experience them. By placing the bot in a world in which it can also use, share and experience things, are we more likely to be able to create a true AI, or even see one emerge, than in some stand-alone computer program?

So this for me is the real cause for optimism. Through the creation of virtual worlds, and their use for as varied roles as virtual meetings, simulation, training and marketing, we may also be creating the environment in which not only will a Turing-capable chatbot be more likely, but a 'true' artificial intelligence as well.

PART 3

Transformations

CHAPTER 5

Getting to the heart of things

Monoclonal antibodies – tackling intractable diseases

Roger McFadden

here is a popular saying in pharmacology that goes along the lines of: 'A drug that does not cause side-effects is a drug that does not work.'

No one is quite sure who first said this but – unlike most popular sayings – this one is invariably true. All drugs have the potential to cause side-effects and a quick glance at the British National Formulary (BNF) will confirm this. Some drugs may cause relatively few side-effects, whilst for others the list of unpleasant side-effects is so long that one wonders why anyone would ever prescribe them – let alone take them voluntarily. These latter drugs are often those prescribed for severe, intractable problems where the therapeutic benefit of the drug outweighs the unpleasant side-effects. For example, anti-cancer drugs often cause nausea and vomiting, but this may be tolerated by the patient if it saves or prolongs their life. If a drug for mild pain caused the same side effects, no one would take it – no matter how effective it was.

The mechanisms whereby drugs cause side-effects vary, but frequently a drug aimed at a specific target in the body inadvertently hits a similar target in a different tissue or organ, causing an unwanted effect. Generally, the more specific a drug is for its target, the fewer unwanted side-effects it produces – and vice versa.

With this in mind, we turn to the subject of this brief article – monoclonal antibody therapy. Antibodies, also known as immunoglobulins, are proteins produced by B lymphocytes in response to microbial infection. In the lymph nodes, stimulated by the infection, B lymphocytes multiply rapidly into identical clones and produce identical monoclonal antibodies. These are released into the bloodstream where they circulate and seek out microbial invaders. Each type of microbe has a unique chemical signature or antigen and each antibody produced is highly specific to one type of antigen found on one type of microbe. So in response to an *Escherichia coli* bacterial infection we produce antibodies specific to *Escherichia coli* antigen which would ignore any other species of bacterium or virus.

You can think of antibodies as keys and the microbial antigen as a lock – each key being specific for just one lock. Antibodies binding to the microbial antigen will inactivate the microbe whilst stimulating other immune cells such as macrophages to attack the invader.

Given the problem that many drugs are lacking in specificity for their targets whilst antibodies are incredibly specific, would it not be a wonderful development if we could somehow make antibodies into drugs? This idea of directing drugs more accurately to their target has long intrigued pharmacologists. In the early part of the twentieth century, the German Nobel laureate Paul Ehrlich envisaged a 'magic bullet' therapy that would deliver drugs directly to the site of disease. The technology was not available to Ehrlich, but in 1975, in their seminal paper, Kohler and Milstein described a technique for producing monoclonal antibodies that won them a share of the Nobel Prize for medicine.

With the development of the new science of genetic engineering, the stage was now set and research started into the production of artificial antibodies that could recognise specific targets within the human body (rather than just microbial antigen). Genetic engineering involves the manipulation of protein-coding genes to produce modified proteins such as novel antibodies. The manipulated gene can be transferred from one organism into another – perhaps one more suited to producing large amounts of protein such as small mammals, microbes or cells cultured in the laboratory.

The key problem with engineered antibodies is that they may be seen by the recipient's body as foreign antigens and attacked by the host's own antibodies – a problem that plagued the early days of antibody therapy. Fortunately, the problem of innate immunogenicity was eventually resolved and current monoclonal antibodies produce less of an immune response than their predecessors. Many antibodies are produced by combining murine (mouse) and human antibodies. These are the chimeric and humanised monoclonal antibodies which are around 65% and 95% human protein respectively. Other monoclonal antibodies are 100% human protein but will still have been produced by genetic engineering.

Cancer has always been a difficult pathology to target with drugs because cancer cells are in most respects the same as the rest of our trillions of other cells. So it is difficult for drugs to differentiate between normal cells and cancerous cells. There are, however, some subtle differences and monoclonal antibodies are the ideal drugs to target these differences. In certain types of breast cancer, for example, the proliferation of cancerous cells is caused by the malfunction of Her-2/neu receptors. Trastuzumab (Herceptin®) binds to and blocks these receptors from the effects of circulating growth factors thus reducing the rate of proliferation of cancerous cells.

Had he been alive today, Ehrlich would have seen his 'magic bullet' vision fulfilled with monoclonal antibodies that deliver anti-cancer drugs exclusively to cancerous cells currently undergoing clinical trials. Tositumomab (Bexxar®) and ibritumomab tiuxetan (Zevalin®) deliver radioactive iodine-131 and yttrium-90 respectively, exclusively to cancerous

CD20 B lymphocytes in non-Hodgkin's lymphoma. Only the cancerous cells targeted by the antibodies are affected by these radioactive isotopes.

There have also been significant developments in the treatment of rheumatoid arthritis. It is a complex and difficult disease to treat but many and diverse disease modifying anti-rheumatic drugs (DMARDs) are now available, including monoclonal antibodies such as rituximab (MabThera®) and adalimumab (Humira®). Another intractable chronic disease that shows promise of responding to monoclonal antibody therapy is multiple sclerosis. Although not providing a cure, natalizumab (Tysabri®) has been proven to reduce the number of new lesions in patients with highly active relapsing-remitting multiple sclerosis.

The future of monoclonal antibody therapy is exciting because the technology has the potential to treat diseases that are intractable to current drugs. Antibodies have an almost infinite antigen recognition capacity, so it should theoretically be possible to engineer a monoclonal antibody to any selected target – although finding therapeutically responsive targets is not always that easy. Merely binding to a target does not guarantee a clinically significant therapeutic effect.

As we have seen, whilst some monoclonal antibodies can bind to specific targets and block activity related to those targets, others act as carriers, delivering drugs and cytotoxic compounds to those targets. Current research is exploring the grafting of antibodies specific for tumour cells to enzymes that have the capacity to activate otherwise inert drugs (pro-drugs). This technology is called antibody-directed enzyme pro-drug therapy (ADEPT) and will allow the use of relatively toxic anti-cancer drugs that do not become activated until at the site of enzymic activation in the tumour.

The potential of monoclonal antibodies gives us good reason to be optimistic because of their potential to treat currently intractable diseases – and they are one of the finest demonstrations of human ingenuity in the field of medicine.

Genome sequencing – reading the Book of Life

Mark Pallen

iving things are complex and highly variable. The poet Gerard Manley Hopkins captured just a small part of this when he wrote of 'brinded cows … rose-moles all stipple upon trout that swim … chestnut falls; finches' wings'. Yet beneath all this complexity, all living things share pretty much the same language for recording the instructions needed to build them: their DNA, written in the same alphabet of four characters, A, C, T and G.

Just as all the plays or poems of Shakespeare arise from a sequence of letters or all Beethoven's symphonies from a series of notes, all of life's complexity and history – the very Book of Life itself – is written in sequences of just those four characters. Every organism carries its own edition of the book, in the complete set of DNA sequences known as its 'genome'.

A major breakthrough in reading the Book of Life came in the late 1970s, thanks to the work of British scientist, Fred Sanger – one of just four researchers to win two Nobel Prizes. Sanger won his second Nobel Prize for devising a technique for reading the sequence of a DNA molecule. Although Sanger, now in his nineties, has long since retired to his Cambridgeshire home, his technique, now simply called 'Sanger sequencing', soon swept into laboratories across the world and catalysed a heady quarter-century of advances in molecular biology – from creative bioengineering to cataloguing biodiversity. What is more, steady technical progress, including automation, improved the efficiency and ease of use of Sanger's original sequencing technology.

Within a few years of inventing his sequencing method, Sanger and his team showed that his technique could be used to sequence the genomes of viruses and even the genome of an unusual bacterium that powers our cells, the mitochondrion. To do this, Sanger pioneered an approach known as whole-genome shotgun sequencing, which involves ripping a genome into many small fragments, randomly sequencing lots and lots of these and then assembling them all into a single complete sequence – in effect, completing a vast molecular jigsaw puzzle.

In the mid-1990s, our efforts to read the Book of Life took another step forward, when a US team, including Ham Smith and Craig Venter, showed that the whole-genome shotgun approach could be used to sequence the complete genomes of free-living bacteria. Their approach was soon adopted by sequencing centres around the world, where it was applied to many of mankind's most fearsome microbial adversaries – from the cause of the Black Death (*Yersinia pestis*) to that of the White Plague (*Mycobacterium tuberculosis*). Whole-genome shotgun sequencing was even adopted for large genomes, like those of fruit flies or humans. As a result, we now have, captured within our computers, the inner workings of representative strains of every bacterial species that can infect humans or our domesticated plants and animals. Plus we now have genome sequences from all the model organisms that scientists rely on: yeast, worms, flies, mice, chickens etc.

It was great to live through a decade of heady progress in genomics, which revolutionised biology. But ten years after Smith and Venter's breakthrough, half a decade into the new millennium, there were still problems. Genome sequencing remained so costly, time-consuming and technically demanding that it was confined to specialised sequencing centres, rather than undertaken by experts on the organisms being sequenced. Each project seemed more like an Apollo mission than routine science, so that arguments raged over which strains or species should be sequenced first. And genome sequencing as a diagnostic exercise seemed a long way off.

A few years ago, this all began to change, with the arrival of 'next-generation sequencing' (also called 'high-throughput sequencing'). This umbrella term covers a number of fundamentally new approaches to DNA sequencing that deliver sequence data a hundred times more quickly and a hundred times more cheaply than conventional Sanger sequencing. So we are now experiencing a new rush of revolutionary optimism – suddenly, projects that could only be dreamt of have become eminently feasible and there is a feeling that we can sequence anything!

What will this brave new world look like, where we can sequence anything we want to? In my own field of bacteriology, it now possible to envisage a time in the not too distant future when we will be able to genome-sequence bacteria as soon as we isolate them from patients, providing us with a detailed read-out of their potential to cause disease or resist antibiotics plus a molecular fingerprint showing how they are related to similar bacteria from the same location or even from the other side of the world. In doing so, we will gain a fine-grained view of the patterns of spread, tracking MRSA or *Clostridium difficile* or *Mycobacterium tuberculosis* as they spread through our communities and hospitals. With the resulting leap forward in medical intelligence, we will be able to target finite infection control resources in the most efficient way possible.

But beyond that, there is growing optimism that we will not even have to bother to grow bacteria any more. Instead, we will just sequence all the DNA in clinical specimens, whether from sputum, swabs or even pus (ironically bringing us full circle, as DNA was first discovered in surgical pus!). Most of the sequences we recover will be irrelevant to disease, coming from the human host or from friendly bacteria that live on us, but the astonishing throughput of the new sequencing technologies means that we will also be able to recover near-complete sequences of the bacteria that cause disease.

When applied to human genomes, which are around a thousand times larger than bacterial genomes, there is much hope that next-generation sequencing will usher in an era of personal genomics, where an individual's tendency to develop any given disease or react well or badly to any given drug can be read in their very own version of the Book of Life. Such optimism currently has to be tempered by a heavy dose of realism – for example, at the moment, we understand only a small fraction of the genetic determinants of something as apparently simple as a person's height. But with the likelihood that sometime in the next few years it will become possible to sequence anyone's genome for less than $1,000, it is hard to hold back a sense of growing confidence that we will one day pin down all the genetic determinants of disease, as well as unravel what happens when the Book of Life becomes garbled and corrupted during the growth of a cancer.

Another exciting prospect is that high-throughput sequencing will help unravel the specific genetic changes that made us human – the changes that occurred in the human genome during the 6 million years since our lineage split from that our closest living relative, the chimpanzee. We already have a draft chimp genome but now face a 'needle in a haystack' problem in working out which of the tens of millions of changes between human and chimp genomes made us, as Alexander Pope put it, 'a being darkly wise, and rudely great'. Yet the problem has now been rendered finite! It may take several generations of scientists to sift through the evidence, but we can be confident we will one day identify the crucial changes that made us human.

In fact, with high-throughput sequencing, DNA's Book of Life is now even expanding encompassing the Book of the Dead, in that genome sequences can now be recovered not just from dead organisms, but even from those long extinct. On Darwin's two-hundredth 'birthday' in February 2009, Swedish biologist Svante Paabo and his team announced that they had obtained a draft genome sequence from Neanderthals. Neanderthal sequences have been mined for clues as to what our evolutionary cousins were like – we already know that some Neanderthals had pale skin and red hair, blood group O and variations in sense of taste similar to those seen in modern humans. But one statistic from the Neanderthal genome project stands as testament to the astonishing throughput of next-generation sequencing – most DNA recovered from Neanderthal samples was microbial in origin, so to get the equivalent of one Neanderthal genome sequence (3 billion characters), the team had to sequence a total of 68 billion characters!

But for some people, the answer to the question, 'What will you do when you can sequence anything?' provides ample evidence that the quirkiness of human life survives into this bright new future! In an attempt to answer the question 'How many species inhabit our immediate surroundings?', a group of genome biologists has just published paper describing high-throughput sequencing of DNA recovered from windscreen splatter! It is hard to imagine how they got funding for that! Whimsy aside, I remain confident that in the coming years we will read ever more of the Book of Life and I am optimistic that in doing so we will shed light on humanity's most pressing practical problems and deepest existential issues – why do we get sick and what makes us human?

Crop science – meeting the global food challenge

David Pink

wo fairly alarming statements were made at the UN Food and Agriculture Organization's 'World Food Security' conference in June 2008. The Secretary-General of the UN, Ban Ki-moon, said that food production would need to increase by 50% by 2030 to meet rising demand and the Director-General of the Food and Agriculture Organisation, Jacques Diouf, stated that food production would need to double by 2050 to feed an estimated world population of nine billion people. Although there has been some debate as to whether these projections will prove entirely correct, there is little disagreement that feeding the world's increasing population represents a huge global challenge in the face of climate change and reducing resources.

On the face of it, this looks to be a cause for pessimism rather than optimism. However, I am confident that agricultural scientific research will rise to the challenge of feeding the world's population.

Agricultural research has a good track record of success. Global agricultural production has climbed above the rate of population growth in the past four decades, more than doubling, with only an 8% increase in the use of land for agriculture. The basis of this success has been the huge improvement in productivity of our crops. The application of genetic research in plant breeding has made an important contribution to this increase in production and it has been estimated that 50% of the gains in yield in many crops during the twentieth century was attributable to improved varieties, with the other 50% due to improvements in agronomy, crop protection and engineering. I believe that genetics will continue to deliver improvements at the same or greater rate, enabling yield to keep pace with demand.

However, during the twentieth century varieties were bred for growing in increasingly high input forms of agriculture, so the increases of the last half of the century were achieved at an ecological cost – and only with heavy use of energy and oil inputs. In the face of diminishing resources of fossil fuels and the impact their use has on the climate, this is unsustainable. The challenge of producing sufficient food for an increasing world population needs to be achieved by a 'new agriculture' that does not compromise the ability of future generations to meet their needs. This will require the development of 'lower input' production systems, embracing solutions from across the spectrum of current production methods, and the development of new production methods which require less energy and fossil fuel resources whilst still maintaining yield and quality. To do this we will need new crop varieties adapted to grow in such systems.

Why should crop geneticists and breeders be able to deliver the varieties needed for the new agriculture? There are two reasons: one historical, the other current.

During the twentieth century it was realised that breeding new crop varieties selected to perform well under high input systems was leading to an erosion of genetic diversity as the new varieties replaced the older, locally adapted ones. This was further exacerbated by the globalisation of commercial plant breeding, which aimed to produce varieties adapted to as large a growing region as possible in order to maximise the economic return on breeding efforts.

In order to counter this loss of diversity, plant genetic resource collections comprising old varieties and accessions of wild crop relatives were established in 'gene banks' for many crops. These included the world's staple food crops such as wheat and rice and also crops important for a healthy diet such as the collections of field vegetables maintained by the Genetic Resources Unit at the University of Warwick. Many of these plant genetic resources evolved or were selected to grow in relatively low input systems, so they represent a strategic resource for the traits now required for the 'new agriculture'. However, two factors potentially limit the exploitation of the diversity maintained in plant genetic resource collections.

First, although gene banks have done an excellent job in conserving crop diversity (for many crops we have many thousands of accessions), this has presented a problem in terms of accessing the variation in the collections. Because of the cost and effort required, for most traits it is not possible to carry out an assessment of every accession to identify which has the most beneficial phenotype. This problem has been partially addressed by the development of 'core collections' or diversity sets which are sub-samples of the whole collection, representing as much of the geographical and crop diversity as possible. Although these are generally of a size that can be phenotypically screened for traits of interest, their use does not favour the identification of alleles which are rare within the gene pool – and in many cases it will be these rare alleles that we require.

The second potential limitation of gene banks is that they do not conserve genes but rather conserve combinations of genes found in the accessions of old varieties and wild species. This means that a potentially beneficial and valuable gene/allele is combined with other genes/alleles, many of which determine a deleterious phenotype. For example, in wild species accessions there is often a need for a long programme of backcrossing to separate the desired beneficial allele from linked undesirable alleles.

Despite the above qualifications, the forethought of crop scientists in the twentieth century has provided us with the strategic resources for the breeding of the varieties needed for the agriculture of the twenty-first century. I am confident that the development of new technologies in genetics and genomics will enable us to exploit these collections in a more targeted and scientific way, allowing us to meet the challenges ahead.

Crop scientists and plant breeders have already begun to respond to the challenges of breeding new varieties in a more targeted manner with the development of technologies such as marker assisted selection (MAS), in which selection is carried out on the genotype of the plant rather than the phenotype. This has enabled increased efficiency in breeding for quantitative traits which are strongly influenced by environment.

Many of the improvements brought about by crop breeding are incremental, building upon the most recent improvements (ie the currently 'best' varieties). However, I am not optimistic that technologies which provide incremental improvements, important though they are, will allow us fully to meet the global food challenge articulated by Ban-Ki moon and Jacques Diouf – this requires a step change. In my view, this step change was initiated with the publishing of the Arabidopsis genome sequence in 2000.

Arabidopsis was the first plant genome to be sequenced. It took more than four years of work by researchers in the US, Europe and Japan and cost several million pounds. The development of 'next generation' sequence technologies is now moving ahead rapidly and the cost and speed of genotype sequencing has been drastically improved. As the technology develops it will become feasible to sequence many individual genomes, such as the accessions held in plant genetic resource collections, thereby assessing the genetic variation between individuals directly.

This is driving new developments in 'next generation' genetics, such as genome wide association (GWA) or association mapping, which looks for associations between phenotypes of interest and the DNA sequence variation present in the whole of an individual's genome. By using such techniques we will be able take a wider view of genetic variation within the collections. This will allow us to identify those accessions possessing novel alleles which determine the improved performance needed, in traits such as nutrient and water use efficiency, resistance to pests and diseases etc.

We need investment to fund data generation and the bio-informatics capability to handle the data sets. If we get it, I believe that current and future developments in genetics based on 'next generation' sequencing technology will allow crop scientists to 'mine' the crop genetic resources collected in the twentieth century for the alleles needed for breeding the varieties for the twenty-first century.

Some of these beneficial alleles will be found in historic domesticated accessions of landraces and older varieties. These will have to be 're-domesticated' into modern varieties with the desired quality characteristics. Others will only be found in wild species relatives of our crops and will need to be brought in to our domesticated crops. In either case, because these beneficial alleles will be identified through DNA sequence variation, this will provide the molecular markers to allow plant breeders to carry out targeted domestication/re-domestication of these beneficial alleles.

So rather than considering the statements by Ban-Ki moon and Jacques Diouf as all gloom and doom, I look at them as a huge driver for the continued development of crop genetics. I am optimistic that crop scientists will provide the scientific knowledge and tools to create the new crop varieties needed to meet the global food challenge. Whether that provides sufficient food for every global citizen in 2050 will be (as it is today) dependent on socio-political issues such as equitable food distribution, land use and changes to people's diet – but I am not going to comment on my level of optimism regarding this.

Stem cell science – revolutionising the future of medicine

Jon Frampton

Of course I would say that I am optimistic about the prospects offered by stem cell science – how could I say otherwise as a Professor of Stem Cell Biology? But I am, and I firmly believe that the application of our rapidly expanding knowledge about stem cells will revolutionise the future of medicine – though it will not all happen at once, and there certainly will not be a moment when the new technology takes over. As in all science and medicine, things happen in small, incremental steps that add to, rather than replace, the status quo.

Ironically, perhaps, I spend quite a lot of my time playing down the prospects of stem cell related 'cures', at least as they become overblown by a very small number of unscrupulous researchers and journalists looking for the latest front-page splash. One of my fears is that people will become disillusioned with the researchers and clinicians who are working so hard to find out more about stem cells and how they can be used to improve health.

Worse still, I worry that false hope is so often being given to those who are desperate to find a cure for their own or a relative's illness. This all too often results in their spending large amounts of money that they may not be able to afford on bogus therapies that have absolutely no basis in scientific fact and certainly have not undergone the rigorous testing that is required of any new treatment in countries like the UK.

So, why is my outlook positive? Quite simply, because I believe that the application of stem cell science will work; it is just a matter of getting the details right. In fact, and in answer to the common criticism that nothing has been delivered yet by stem cell scientists, there are already many examples of highly successful therapies that rely on the use of stem cells – and there are some tremendous advances just round the corner.

The most obvious existing clinical use of stem cells is bone marrow transplantation, which was first attempted in the 1950s and has become a very successful treatment for a range of diseases, mainly associated with the blood. Our vast knowledge of the nature of the stem cells involved, gained over the last four decades, is not only leading to improvements in such transplantations but is also increasing the numbers of people who have access to this treatment. And there are more examples – grafts used to replace skin destroyed by burns or a damaged cornea on the outer surface of the eye involve the production of cells from stem cells contained within these tissues. The recent replacement of a young woman's windpipe damaged as the result of a tuberculosis infection is another, much publicised, example of this treatment.

Yet more exciting therapies for conditions involving loss or damage of particular organs or tissues, especially those that occur with advancing age, lie just round the corner. For example, a number of problems associated with joint or bone degeneration may well be treatable using the same sorts of stem cells that were used to produce that replacement windpipe, whilst specific cells that cover the retina at the back of the eye and whose failure leads to the condition known as macular degeneration, a common cause of blindness in the elderly, can be obtained directly from stem cells. These are very likely to be undergoing clinical trials within a few years.

But this is just the tip of the iceberg, and that is not just because more ways will be found to replace more cell types in different organs. It has become clear quite recently that an understanding of stem cell biology has other potentially profound implications in the treatment of disease. Most notably, it is now widely believed that most cancers – or at least some component of them that is responsible for their maintenance and often for their resistance to classical treatments such as chemotherapy – have stem cell properties. Our rapidly growing understanding of these properties opens up totally new avenues for the discovery of highly selective drugs that will target the cancer cells and could result in their total eradication.

One advance developed over the last three years stands out as being revolutionary. The greatest hope in stem cell science, but one that has generated most disquiet and objection on religious and ethical grounds, is that so-called embryonic stem cells – derived from embryos and with all of the potential of that early stage in our development – can provide a limitless supply of any of the 200 or more cell types of our bodies. However, apart from the ethical issues that have led many to question this approach, embryonic stem cells have one big limitation: the cells derived from them are unlikely to be perfectly matched to the donor. As a consequence, any replacement therapy will have to be accompanied by drugs that dampen the response of the patient's immune system.

But what if embryonic stem cells could be made that match every individual, so that truly personalised medicine would become a reality? A number of options have been considered to achieve this goal, but the real breakthrough came in 2006 when the Japanese researcher Shinya Yamanaka showed that it is possible to convert cells, such as those in our skin, to become like embryonic stem cells. These cells are referred to as induced pluripotent stem cells, or iPS cells for short, and they offer the real prospect of limitless cell replacement for all – with the added advantage of not having involved the use of an embryo. Of course, there are many details yet to be ironed out, but progress in this area of stem cell science is nothing if not meteoric!

Much is still to be done in stem cell science, both to capitalise on the discoveries so far and to enable them to be shifted from the bench to the bedside. Nevertheless, I am very confident that in my lifetime there will be a growing array of treatments that utilise our knowledge of these rather special cells, and that by the time my children are themselves middle-aged stem cell therapy will be taken for granted as part of the portfolio of options available to all.

Immunology – glimpsing the Holy Grail

Peter Lane

In 1975, when I went to Edinburgh to study medicine, our understanding of basic mechanisms of disease was quite rudimentary, and the development of new therapies by pharmaceutical companies was mainly based around screening of small compounds, which were then formulated as pills or for injection. Around this time, however, two fundamental discoveries changed the science of medicine. First was the capacity to decipher the DNA encoding our genes; second were techniques to make antibodies of exquisite mono specificity (monoclonal antibodies). These two events catalysed the birth of molecular medicine, and the further development of DNA technology has opened the door to understanding how genes and the proteins that they encode work.

The key to this rapid progress is the fast-moving pace of technology.

From early beginnings in the 1970s when only a few hundred letters of DNA code could be deciphered, by the turn of the twenty-first century the entire human genome of 3 billion letters was unravelled. By comparing the human genome with those of other animals, it has been possible to gain an understanding of when genes evolved, and also how new genes evolved to develop new functions.

In the immune system, this has been particularly useful for identifying genes that control the survival of memory CD4 T cells. CD4 T cells play a central role in our immune response to infection and underlie the success of the vaccination strategies in the last century that eliminated or at least substantially controlled many otherwise lethal infections. Because the development of CD4 memory occurred late in the evolution of the modern immune system, the genes that control CD4 memory development can readily be spotted by pinpointing newly evolved genes.

Again, the power of modern DNA technology has been instrumental in proving that identified genes really are playing the roles that we have supposed. The technology of making animals deficient in particular genes has allowed us to test and refine our ideas of how individual genes alone and in combination with other genes control the development of immune memory. The combination of these genetic tools with approaches that visualise how cells interact to generate immune responses is a very powerful strategy for elucidating how biological systems work.

Why is this relevant to advances in medicine? Well, the key to successful treatment of human diseases of the immune system is to target pathways specific to the pathology. Successful transplantation depends at present on drug treatment to suppress organ rejection; early treatments used drugs that were non-specific in their effects, suppressing the natural defences of the immune system as well as the specific rejection of the transplanted organ, with the consequence that side-effects like infection were common. Modern immunosuppression is more targeted to the specific immune reaction against the transplanted organ, but unfortunately we still have not learnt how to allow the transplanted organ to survive indefinitely without prolonged immunosuppression.

This is something of a 'holy grail' in immunology, but we know that it is an achievable goal, because during pregnancy the mother 'tolerates' the developing child without mounting a damaging immune response. We have been afforded glimpses of the processes that might permit this inbuilt immunosuppression, and I am optimistic that the next decade will elucidate the details of how it works, bringing forward the goal of re-establishing tolerance not only in the context of transplantation, but perhaps also on the wider scale of autoimmune diseases such as rheumatoid arthritis.

Protein molecules – solving a fundamental mystery

Michael Overduin

 cientists have discovered the parts list of over a thousand living and extinct organisms over the past decade. We can now number our genes, proteins and cells, and can see their individual shapes in motion. One of the greatest opportunities in biomedical research today is to understand how these various jigsaw pieces fit together. My optimism for science stems from the development of new technologies that allow us to see how biological molecules are assembled and organised together. Ultimately, these insights will allow us to understand living processes in much greater detail and to design smarter drugs to intervene more effectively.

My laboratory at the University of Birmingham studies how proteins behave on membrane surfaces. Membranes are oily layers that surround our cells and organelles.

They provide organisation, dividing our cells into various compartments where different activities occur. Understanding membranes is critical for drug discovery research, as most drug molecules and the proteins they bind are found in membranes. Studying the lipids and proteins in membranes has been a major challenge that has frustrated researchers for decades because they are sticky, unstable and hard to work with. Finding a general solution to convert membrane proteins into well-behaved forms is crucial for further progress, and would enable a range of new targets to be studied and exploited for therapeutic intervention into a wide range of diseases.

Our research team and collaborators from the University of Warwick have devised a revolutionary way to purify and study membrane proteins using a new 'bionanotechnology' system. We added a polymer to cellular membranes to separate their many components into tiny discs that are 10 million times smaller than a computer CD. We named the new nanometre-size disc a 'SMALP' as an acronym of 'styrene maleic acid lipid particle'. The SMALP components are soluble, stable and easy to work with, being composed of natural lipids found in our own bodies and a polymer previously used to deliver cancer drugs to tumours.

Each SMALP contains about eleven lipid molecules and a membrane protein with its activity and structure intact. The tiny discs are stable enough to be purified, heated, frozen, dried or stored. They are ideal for many experiments that reveal the function and structure of the protein inside. We first tried two bacterial proteins that work as an enzyme and light absorber. Both proteins could easily be placed into the nanoparticles, and their folded structure and binding and enzymatic activities were fully preserved. We are now investigating how the method can be applied to other proteins, including drug receptors that have previously been difficult to obtain and study. As a result of this work, several pharmaceutical companies have already expressed an interest in using SMALPs.

Another project in our lab focuses on seeing how proteins encounter and reshape membranes. Different types of membranes surround each of our cells and the dozens of tiny organelles that inhabit them. For example, the Golgi apparatus serves as the cell's post office by processing and packaging proteins for delivery to destinations such as the cell surface. Using superconducting magnets and high power microscopes, we have been able to visualise how individual proteins reshape the Golgi membrane into thin tubes that are pinched off to deliver 'mail' to the surface of a human cell. We were also able to pinpoint the effects of dozens of genetic alterations on this protein that have been sequenced in cancerous tissues, including lung tumours, providing an understanding of the molecular consequences of these mutations.

In a third project we are studying how protein molecules fold up into three-dimensional structures inside membranes. This folding question has remained one of the fundamental mysteries of biological science, and is now known to involve a protein machine known as BAM, an acronym for 'barrel assembly machine'. The BAM complex includes five proteins which sit together in the outer membrane of bacteria, including a number of pathogens, as well as in chloroplasts and mitochondria. Within this machine, we are identifying the positions of each of the five proteins and their thousands of atoms. This represents our most complicated challenge yet, in that the assembly machine sits on the membrane, receives dozens of unfolded proteins from delivery proteins, and weaves them into intricate barrel shapes inside the oily environment of the membrane. These proteins are required for the infectious cycle, and understanding how they form will provide new opportunities to design antibiotics for a wide range of pathogenic bacteria.

A final project which really excites me is a new computer program we are developing with a group in California. Although humans are the walking, breathing result of over 20,500 genes working together, we have little idea of what the individual jobs are of each protein produced by our genes. Our program scans the surface of each protein and predicts whether it can interact with membranes, proteins or small molecules. Ultimately, intelligent programs like this will take us to places where our data is sparse and the space vast.

Genome sequences –
a snub to bigots

Robin May

We are living through a silent revolution. In hospitals, universities, research centres and pharmaceutical companies, a new age of genetics is already transforming lives. The revolution is in genomics, the study of all the genes that, together, make up individuals. The plummeting cost of 'reading' (sequencing) genetic information, coupled with huge advances in computer power, mean that we are about to enter an age when having a copy of one's own genome sequence is as common as carrying a mobile phone is today.

The era of the personalised genome raises unprecedented ethical dilemmas: discovering that one's child carries three predisposing mutations for early-onset Alzheimer's disease, for instance, or worrying that every moment of mental confusion marks the start of your genetically predetermined schizo-phrenia. But it is also, in my opinion, a cause for huge optimism.

First, as a tool to deepen our understanding of both normal and pathological processes, whole-genome sequences are unparalleled. Classical epidemiological and pedigree ('family tree') analyses have shown that many, perhaps most, diseases have at least some genetic component. Often these are so-called polygenic traits, reflecting the complex interplay between many genes at different sites in the genome

It is almost impossible to identify such genes using existing approaches, but the ability to compare whole genome sequences between large groups of patients and healthy control subjects will render such work commonplace. As a result, it is certainly not over-optimistic to expect massive advances in our understanding of cardiovascular disease, mental health and allergy within the next few years.

As a tool for population-level studies of disease traits, whole-genome data will be a superb resource. But it is likely to be equally revolutionary on an individual level, bringing with it the remarkable prospect of 'personalised medicine'. It is already well established that individual differences in physiology drastically alter the effect of therapeutic drugs; a medication that is effective in one patient can be useless, or even harmful, in another. Thus far, however, our approach to such variability has been a far-from-optimal 'suck-it-and-see' strategy; if drug A fails, then switch the patient to drug B, whilst hoping that neither A nor B generate dangerous side-effects.

How much better it would be if one could assess the patient before treatment and determine which drugs will work and which should be avoided. In a small number of recent cases, a simplistic version of personalised medicine has already started to be employed. In some breast cancer patients, for instance, biopsy tissue is examined for the presence of particular hormone receptors which, if present, render the tumour sensitive to the hormone therapy, an approach which would be useless in tumours lacking the same receptor. And in 2005, the US FDA approved the release of the drug BiDil for the treatment of cardiovascular complaints specifically in black patients, as a result of the observation that African-Americans generally respond poorly to other treatments for congestive heart failure.

The availability of whole genome sequences, however, will usher in an era of truly 'personal' medicine that is likely to transform everything from drug prescriptions to psychotherapy. A world in which GPs make drug selections and decisions about dosing based on each patient's unique genetic profile will not only improve the efficacy of thousands of drugs, but also holds the potential to make a huge reduction in the thousands of people who are hospitalised each year in the UK due to side-effects from prescribed drugs.

Lastly, I am optimistic that whole genome sequencing will be the final nail in the coffin of discrimination. Immeasurable column inches have been devoted to the prospect of genetic sequencing leading to people being unfairly 'pigeon-holed' based on the presence of markers for low intelligence, criminality, violent behaviour and so forth. However, in reality, the extraordinary rainbow of genetics that comprises the human genome is the ultimate snub to bigots the world over. Whole genome sequencing will reveal the black African in every white supremacist, the Jewish ancestry in every Islamic fundamentalist and perhaps even the gay man in every homophobe.

Perhaps the greatest achievement of whole genome sequencing will lie not in showing us the influence of genetic variation in our lives, but in revealing the way in which nurture, rather than nature, turns us into the people that we are.

The power of vaccination – improving global health

Yvonne Perrie

According to the World Health Organization (WHO), the two public health interventions that have had the greatest impact on the world's health are the supply of clean water and vaccines.

We know that vaccines are capable of preventing death on a wide scale and can offer populations 'herd immunity'; that is to say that if there is a small group of people who are not/can not be immunised, these people can still be protected from infection by blocking the transmission of the disease through the vaccinated group. However, achieving 'herd immunity' relies on public support for vaccination programmes. Recently, public support for vaccination has been significantly damaged by bad press and poor science – which has cast a shadow over the safety of vaccines.

In particular, the controversy related to the safety of the combined measles, mumps and rubella (MMR) vaccine stemming from proposed links with autism has had a detrimental impact on the protection of children from these diseases within the UK. Whilst most of the researchers who initially proposed this link subsequently retracted their speculations, the damage in terms of public confidence has been done. We have yet to recover from this, to the extent that there are areas within the UK where we are below the recommended number of vaccinated people needed to block disease outbreaks (recommended at 95% of the population vaccinated in the case of MMR).

However, the evidence is clear: vaccines remain a major success story in healthcare – most dramatically resulting in the eradication of smallpox. Smallpox is a highly contagious viral infection, which is believed to have originated over 3,000 years ago in India or Egypt and is often described as one of the most devastating diseases we have seen. Repeated epidemics have swept continents, killing 30% of those infected and scarring or blinding most that survived, including Queen Mary II of England, Emperor Joseph I of Austria, King Luis of Spain, Tsar Peter of Russia, Queen Ulrika Elenora of Sweden and King Louis XV of France. However, in 1798 Edward Jenner demonstrated that injection of fluid containing a related but milder virus (cowpox) could protect against smallpox. By the 1940s the disease was eliminated in Europe and North America, and in 1967 the WHO launched a global campaign to eradicate smallpox. In 1980, the organisation was officially able to declare, 'the world and its peoples free from endemic smallpox'. Much of this effort should be attributed to the Soviet Union, which first suggested a global effort and which donated over 80% of the vaccines needed.

We also need to recognise the contribution of the pharmaceutical sciences. The smallpox vaccine as a liquid was stable for only two days, which made widespread distribution of the vaccine near impossible. However, preparing the vaccine as a freeze-dried vaccine (where the vaccine is frozen and then dried under vacuum) meant that the vaccines were stable for up to one month without the requirement of refrigeration. The long-term stability of vaccines remains a key factor today – most are still distributed as a freeze-dried product.

Yet despite this success with smallpox, two other infectious diseases, malaria and tuberculosis (TB), remain two of the world's primary killers, and the combination of either of these diseases with HIV is lethal. With TB alone there are some scary statistics: every second someone becomes newly infected with TB; and overall one-third of the world's population is currently infected. Although we have a vaccine for TB, in the form of BCG, which most of us have received during our childhood, and the bulk of deaths occur in developing countries, TB is an increasing global public healthcare concern. Unfortunately, BCG provides only variable protection and is not effective in adults. Therefore we need new, improved vaccines.

There are several laboratories working to develop improved vaccines for TB, including the Centre for Clinical Vaccinology and Tropical Medicine at the University of Oxford, where Dr Helen McShane and Professor Adrian Hill have developed a recombinant based vaccine which is particularly effective when used together with the BCG vaccine. This is currently in phase II clinical trials. Peter Andresen and his group in Statens Serum Institut have also developed a promising new vaccine for TB, and collaborations with our group in Aston University have provided the underpinning information to help this vaccine enter clinical trials early this year. We look forward to the outcome of both these studies as current data for both look very promising.

These are just two examples of the many research programmes tackling this one disease and there remain many other diseases that also must be addressed. Infectious agents are also implicated as causes of cancer and contribute to a variety of malignancies worldwide. Some of the major players in this respect include human polyomaviruses, which can induce brain tumours, herpesvirus, which has been associated with lymphomas, and human papillomaviruses (HPV), which can induce cervical carcinoma. Indeed, the recognition of the connection between the HPV and cervical cancer has resulted in the introduction of cervical cancer vaccine programmes across the UK.

The continuing positive role vaccines can play in improving our global heath is clear, and understanding of the factors which make good vaccines improves every day through a global research effort. We continue to gain

CHAPTER 6

Changing behaviour

HIV/Aids –
a twenty-five-year rollercoaster

Hazel Barrett

In the spring of 2009 media headlines appeared around the world that doctors in Berlin believed they had found a cure for HIV-AIDS. Bone marrow stem cells had been used to treat leukaemia in an HIV-positive male patient. Three years after the treatment the patient had no detectable signs of HIV, leading to the claim that perhaps marrow stem cells were the silver bullet the world had been waiting for in the fight against AIDS.

This highly optimistic story is just one of many that have been reported over the 25-year history of the global HIV-AIDS pandemic that have raised hopes that a cure or vaccine for HIV-AIDS is close. Too often these hopes are dashed. The search for a cure or vaccine for HIV has been a 25-year roller coaster of optimism followed by despair.

The HIV virus was identified in 1983 by the French scientists

Francoise Barre-Sinoussi and Luc Montagnier, work for which they were awarded the Nobel Prize for Medicine in 2008. We are now entering the third decade of the global HIV-AIDS pandemic and a cure or vaccine is as distant as ever. Since the virus was identified the disease has spread to every corner of the globe. In 2008, UNAIDS reported that 33 million people globally were living with the disease, with 2.7 million people newly infected in that year and 2 million dying. Since the beginning of the pandemic it is estimated that 30 million people have died as a result of the infection. These shocking data make this pandemic the most serious that humankind has faced in its history.

AIDS is caused by HIV, which is a lentivirus, a member of the subgroup of the retrovirus family. One of the main characteristics of the lentivirus is its extensive genetic variability. Two types of HIV have been identified, HIV-1 and HIV-2. HIV-1 is more transmissible and more pathogenic than HIV-2. Each of these HIV types contains virologically related groups comprising subtypes. Scientists have to date identified five groups and 20 subtypes of HIV, with the expectation that more will develop. However, one subtype, HIV-1 Group M Subtype C, is responsible for 55–60% of all global infections.

The HIV virus is highly unstable and susceptible to recombining. There are thus many circulating recombinant forms of the virus which have been formed using the genetic structures from two or more HIV subtypes. This occurs when individuals are exposed to different groups and subtypes of the virus. Within HIV-1 Group M, for example, there are at least 15 recombinant circulating forms. Co-infection with divergent HIV-1 strains is relatively frequent, with over 20% of HIV infections in South-east Asia attributed to recombinant circulating forms of HIV. At present no recombinants have been reported between HIV-1 and HIV-2; however, as the number of recombinant viruses increases the chance that they may contribute to a new HIV group is high. In August 2009, scientists announced the discovery of a new type of HIV in a woman from Cameroon, highlighting the need to monitor for the emergence of new types of HIV.

The genetic variability of HIV is a major factor explaining why finding a cure or vaccine for it has been so elusive. Despite unprecedented efforts on vaccine research, it has proven difficult for scientists to produce a vaccine to counter so many subtypes of the virus. In addition, any vaccine would have to be unable to recombine with existing HIV viruses to ensure the vaccine did not accidentally produce new infecting HIV strains.

The nature of HIV infection and the long latency period of the infection is another obstacle to finding a cure or vaccine for the disease. It can be months after initial infection before the human body produces antibodies. This is too late to fight the HIV infection, as by this time the virus has stored itself in 'reservoirs', or anatomical sanctuaries in the body, such as the lymph nodes of the intestines. These 'stored' viruses are not destroyed by the body's immune response, even after many years of antiretroviral (ARV) treatment. This is shown in the reactivation of the virus if ARV treatment is interrupted. If a cure or vaccine is to be effective, access to these 'resting cells' during the latent period of the disease is vital.

As a result of these challenges, there have been many disappointments concerning vaccine development. Following the collapse of a major clinical trial of an AIDS vaccine (V520) by Merck at the end of 2007 (which may have actually increased the chances of people developing AIDS), scientists have become very pessimistic about the possibilities of successfully developing an AIDS vaccine in the short to medium term using current approaches.

In a survey of 35 leading UK and US scientists involved in AIDS research undertaken by *The Independent* newspaper in April 2008, many admitted that effective immunisation against HIV may not be possible. There is a mood of deep pessimism amongst scientists researching AIDS and there is currently much debate on the ethics of spending billions of pounds on researching an AIDS vaccine rather than focussing on prevention and treatment, at a time of increasing transmissible HIV resistance to ARVs.

Science has taught us much about the epidemiology of the HIV-AIDS pandemic. We know the disease is transmitted from person to person in infected bodily fluids, such as by using contaminated needles or having unsafe sexual intercourse with an infected person. HIV-AIDS can thus be classified as a 'lifestyle' disease, linked particularly to intimate sexual behaviour, which is the leading route of transmission of the virus. This means we need to pay greater attention to the economic and social factors that drive risky behaviour and try to understand how these can be effectively altered in a socially acceptable way. As with any lifestyle medical condition, education combined with changing social expectations and norms can lead to behavioural change that reduces the 'risk' environment in which people live, and could ultimately control the spread of HIV.

Behavioural change, especially concerning sexual activity, is not easy to achieve, as the HIV-AIDS pandemic has demonstrated, but it is possible. Some countries in sub-Saharan Africa, the region most severely affected by the pandemic, are reporting stabilisation or declines in HIV prevalence. There is strong evidence that this is attributable to effective changes in sexual behaviour, such as the postponement of sexual debut, reduction in casual sexual relationships and more consistent use of condoms. Effective public health campaigns such as the ABC Approach (where A translates into sexual Abstinence, B is for Be faithful and C stands for use a Condom, for the next letter in the alphabet is D which stands for Death), have been largely responsible for a reduction in risky sexual behaviour in this region.

Education and behavioural change are not easy options. Humans are constantly looking to science and technology to provide solutions so that they do not have to change their behaviour. However, we could stop the spread of HIV-AIDS in its tracks tomorrow before a cure or vaccine is ready and at a fraction of the cost if we changed our behaviour. We just need the will to do so.

Cognitive science and behavioural economics – showing us keys to happiness

Gordon Brown, Neil Stewart and Alex Wood

As cognitive psychologists working at the interface between economics and the psychology of decision-making and choice, we see many reasons for optimism about the future. An increasing understanding of how and why we choose, behave and feel as we do is already improving the well-being of individuals and society.

In previous centuries, mere survival was the focus – enough resources to ensure material security had to be harvested, and many premature deaths occurred due to diseases that were then incurable. However, in a growing number of societies most material needs are now met, and the key causes of death are now not linked to poverty or infectious disease, but rather have behavioural causes – smoking, lack of exercise and poor nutritional choices are growing contributors to premature death. Thus in the twenty-first century, the focus must shift from mastery of the environment to mastery of our cognition.

Psychology and behavioural economics are uniquely well placed to contribute to the behavioural change necessary to reduce waste, effect climate change and increase human well-being and health. Here we describe how, by working with rather than against the grain of human psychology, policy-makers can achieve advances in social, health and economic domains. Specifically, we focus on how research from psychology and behavioural economics can inform both national policy and individual behaviour.

Regarding national policy, a key contribution of recent research has been to show that the pursuit of material wealth will not lead to significant further increases in happiness and well-being. The very poorest people in a rich society such as ours do become happier when they get more money, perhaps as their basic needs are not being fulfilled. However, above this level (about £10,000 per year), money typically explains only around 1 or 2% of individual differences in happiness (this can be contrasted with the 17.5% of happiness variation explicable by individual differences in gratitude – whether a person habitually notices and appreciates the positive in the world).

The same is true of nations. Over 40 years ago, Richard Easterlin noted that increases in national wealth over many decades in the more wealthy countries had not been accompanied by equivalent increases in the average well-being reported by the populations of those countries. The lack of a clear relationship between wealth and well-being has led economists such as Richard Layard and psychologists such as Ed Diener to propose that, instead of wealth, some form of national well-being index should be the focus of social policy.

Although people's happiness depends little on how much they earn, we have found that their happiness is more strongly related to how their income ranks within their particular communities and workplaces. Thus, a person earning £30,000 in an industry where people most people earn less than this amount will, other things being equal, be happier than someone earning the same amount but in another industry where most people earn more. However, a person whose income rose from £30,000 to £40,000 would be no happier if everyone else's income improved by an equal amount (because everyone's relative ranked position would remain unchanged). This 'relative comparison' approach may explain why people do not become happier as societies become richer.

Such findings suggest that if governments aim to increase happiness, they should focus less on improving everyone's income and instead place greater emphasis on goals such as reducing inequality and unemployment. Inequality is related to a variety of social ills and goods (rates of crime, teenage pregnancy etc – the recent book by Richard Wilkinson and Kate Pickett provides a persuasive summary). The effects are large, can affect all segments of society and do not depend on the overall wealth of the society.

We suggest that if people knew of the importance of the effects of inequality in issues that concern them, they would demand more emphasis from politicians on reducing inequality. Similarly, becoming unemployed is devastating to well-being, and in addition to lost income, unemployment erodes a person's identity and sense of self-worth. Improving national happiness may be better achieved by a greater emphasis on preventing unemployment rather than on increasing everyone's income.

In attempting to effect change at the level of individual behaviour, an important principle is to work 'with the grain' of human limitations and preferences, rather than to impose solutions that are at odds with how people naturally make decisions. To illustrate this, consider several examples of how concepts arising from psychology and economics may be utilised by people planning behavioural interventions, or trying to change their own behaviour.

Daniel Kahneman and Amos Tversky provided evidence for a phenomenon known as 'loss aversion'. For example, it is psychologically more painful to lose £100 than it is psychologically pleasurable to gain £100. Such effects generalise to most aspects of life, with almost any possession (eg a coffee mug, time, clean air, an investment) being worth more psychologically when it is already in an individual's possession than when it is not. Such findings are often used intuitively by take-away shop owners, who give free delivery or a 10% reduction for collection. This 10% 'gain' will seem psychologically smaller than the 'loss' of a 10% delivery charge, even though the deal is equivalent. At more socially meaningful levels, people would presumably be more willing to accept a policy framed as a tax discount for recycling, rather than a fine for excess rubbish collection.

Another finding, 'anchoring', is that when people are making financial decisions they 'latch on' to suggested figures, even when such figures are largely arbitrary. For example, one of us (NS) gave hypothetical credit card bills to people. The bills either had prominently stated (and very low) minimum payments or did not (allowing people to pay any amount). The aim of minimum payments is to make people pay off their bills faster, avoiding extra interest charges. However, people who saw the very low payment anchored onto this amount and paid less than people who had a totally free choice about how much they should pay. This exemplifies how an intervention can be dangerous if planned without regard to psychological and behavioural research – the well-meaning attempt to make people pay more on their credit cards may actually lead to them paying less.

In a somewhat similar vein, people show considerable inertia. When presented with options, people tend to stick with the default. For example, requiring people actively to 'opt out' of pension saving schemes or organ donation, rather than requiring them to 'opt in', substantially changes behaviour in what would generally be agreed to be socially desirable direction, yet without removing freedom to choose. This kind of 'nudge' (beautifully reviewed by Richard Thaler and Cass Sunstein in their book of the same name) offers the opportunity for cognitive and economic psychology to improve everyday health-related behaviours and decision-making. Effects of even small behavioural nudges can be strong. For example, merely asking people whether they intend to vote, or whether they plan to buy a car in the next two years, can have a substantial impact on whether those actions actually happen.

One particularly powerful nudge involves providing people with information about 'social norms'. As with income, people judge their own situation in terms of how it related to that of others. For example, one's attitude to one's own alcohol or tobacco consumption is influenced by how much one thinks other people drink or smoke. Many people overestimate the amount of such consumption that other people engage in, and work by Wesley Perkins and others in the US has shown, for example, that providing accurate information about how you are doing worse than other people ('most students drink fewer than four times a week', you drink ten) can reduce average consumption. Thus a more realistic perception of what other people are doing, when they are doing better than you, can encourage more positive behaviour.

However, conversely, it can be harmful to provide people with information about how other people have more bad habits than them. For example, telling people that a large number of people miss hospital appointments (at great cost) can actually increase the number of missed appointments. Carelessly planned drug education programmes can give the impression that drug-taking is common, and by changing the perception of the 'social norm' may lead to increased drug-taking in adolescents. These findings both suggest how psychology and behavioural economics can be used to design interventions and highlight the perils of planning interventions without such input.

To conclude: we are optimistic that in the current century a central objective of education, from childhood on, will come to be the development of understanding regarding cognitive biases that determine our choices and plans in economic and consumer contexts. We hope that one day all citizens will learn about what really leads to happiness and life satisfaction at both societal and individual levels. We look forward to a time in which we can all lead better lives by understanding and working within the limitations of the decision-making and choosing mechanisms that evolution has endowed us with.

We do not know how much things have got worse, but we do know that things can get better. We are optimistic that – with the aid of cognitive science and behavioural economics – they will.

Changing behaviour – and promoting health

David French

In recent years, increasing amounts of information concerning threats to health have been widely available, often leading to health 'scares'. Even though this information is often reasonably accurate, as in the case of the 'obesity epidemic', I am confident that people will continue the trend of leading longer, healthier lives. In addition, I expect my discipline, health psychology, to play a progressively important role in this improvement in public health due to its role in the increasingly productive development of a science of behaviour change.

The major causes of death in the West in the nineteenth century were infectious diseases, which often affected the very young. The public health approaches taken to reduce these diseases, such as improved sanitation and development of antibiotics, were hugely successful.

As a consequence, the majority of deaths are now brought about by chronic diseases such as cancer and cardiovascular disease, which usually occur in later life.

The causes of such diseases are largely behavioural, specifically smoking, eating an unhealthy diet and insufficient physical activity. Major improvements in public health in the twenty-first century will therefore be brought about by changes in lifestyle behaviours: encouraging people not to smoke, to eat less saturated fat and more fruit and vegetables and to be less sedentary.

There are several commonly held ideas about how to bring about changes in people's lifestyle behaviours. These often underlie communications and behaviour change campaigns by bodies such as government or medical charities, or the efforts of individual healthcare professionals. But there is now good evidence that campaigns based on these commonly held ideas of how to change behaviour are, at best, sub-optimal in terms of bringing about lasting changes in lifestyle behaviours.

For instance, it is often thought that people engage in unhealthy behaviours because they lack knowledge that such behaviours are unhealthy. This is only partially true, at best. There is evidence, for example, that people who begin smoking have unrealistic beliefs about how easy it would be to quit: when young smokers are asked if they expect to be smoking at a specified time in the future, many expect to have quit, but when this is followed up few have actually done so. However, most adult smokers are not only aware that smoking is bad for their health but have made at least one unsuccessful attempt to quit and, in many cases, several such unsuccessful attempts. Clearly, knowledge that one's behaviour is unhealthy is not sufficient to bring about behaviour change.

Another approach to changing health-related behaviours is to provide frightening or alarming information about the consequences of these behaviours. There have been a large number of studies on this approach, and the evidence is now clear that effects on behaviour are likely to be limited. It may also be counterproductive: frightening messages may prompt people to derogate the message content or avoid thinking about the unhealthy behaviour altogether, especially when they do not believe they have the ability to alter their behaviour.

Other popular approaches suffer from focusing on the health consequences of health-related behaviour. For instance, whilst it is true that a lack of physical activity results in poorer longer-term health, this is not a terribly motivating reason for most people to be more active. More immediate concerns such as appearance are more likely to initiate behaviour change, and emotional factors such as enjoyment of specific activities are likely to maintain changes made, through newly formed habits.

Equally, feeling that one does not have the capacity to change one's behaviour is often a more important reason for failing to initiate behaviour change than a lack of good reasons for wanting to change. In fact, there is now strong evidence that motivation to change may be necessary but is usually not a sufficient condition to initiate behaviour change – failure to change unhealthy behaviours is often a consequence of people not being good at enacting their good intentions. Behavioural interventions which help people plan their change attempts in detail and make plans about overcoming barriers are proving to be more effective.

Advances in developing a science of behaviour change are numerous. These include a dramatic increase in recent years in both the number and quality of studies evaluating the effects of interventions to alter behaviour, often involving comparison with interventions which have been generally found to be ineffective. However, these intervention studies have resulted in a mass of data which is difficult to evaluate, with inconsistent findings across studies. Nevertheless, the development of systematic literature reviewing, which involves identifying studies and integrating results with as little bias as possible, has helped identify general trends in which kinds of behavioural interventions are most effective.

Although the use of systematic literature reviewing is useful, it can be a blunt tool, largely because the contents of behavioural interventions are so poorly described. For example, it is not terribly useful to note that 'counselling' may help people increase their physical activity following heart attacks if counselling is defined differently in different studies.

My confidence in the future of this area arises from recent responses to this problem, namely in attempts to develop classification schemes of the precise contents of behavioural interventions. For example, does an intervention involve setting behavioural goals (of what sort), do participants in these studies receive feedback (of what sort), and do they make plans (of what sort) about how to bring about behaviour change? These classification schemes not only allow the effects of interventions on behaviour to be quantified, but also allow estimates to be made of how large these effects are, depending on the presence or absence of specific intervention techniques.

The identification of which techniques are effective and which are ineffective also allows development in theories of behaviour change. There is increasing theorising about the processes involved in behaviour change and maintenance after people have formed intentions to change, about how people regulate their own behaviour and about which approaches are likely to lead to successful self-regulation. The evidence from previous intervention studies has allowed the predictions of previous theories to be tested, and the predictions generated by new theories can be tested in future intervention studies.

Some people believe this approach is too individually focused and ignores the role of social context in the patterning of health-related behaviours. Environment plays a central role in shaping human behaviour. Where food high in fat, sugar and salt is readily available but fresh fruit and vegetables are not, people will tend to make unhealthy choices. The approach described can include the scientific study of – and intervention with – environmental and social determinants of health, such as opportunities for walking safely instead of driving and the use of taxation and advertising to reduce smoking behaviour.

Some other readers may feel uncomfortable with the ethics of attempting to manipulate human behaviour in this way. Nevertheless, increasing our understanding of the most effective ways of promoting healthier behaviours – and the unintended harmful consequences of these attempts – will allow more effective use of public money to improve health. We are at last making progress in one of the most important challenges for contemporary science: how to help people alter their behaviour to enjoy longer and healthier lives.

Medical imaging technology – our brain is our future

Gemma Calvert

Global warming, overpopulation, droughts, famines, species pushed to the brink of extinction by deforestation and over-fishing – one may well ask what is there to be sanguine about? The future of the earth and humankind is not, I believe, in our hands, but in our uniquely human brain. Here, I wish to highlight insights from the fields of cognitive neuroscience, brain imaging and neurology that are helping us to understand ourselves – our needs, desires and the forces that shape and determine our behaviour. Our challenge is to find a way to use this knowledge and to harness these insights to shape the fate of our planet and future generations.

In the early 1990s, the introduction of a new medical imaging technology revolutionised our understanding of brain function – allowing us to for the first time to 'see' inside the working human brain. Functional magnetic resonance imaging (FMRI) monitors changes in oxygen-based energy consumption across the whole brain, indirectly revealing the brain areas involved in a particular task and how they are modulated by different external contexts, with exquisite precision. But how has this helped us to understand ourselves?

Psychologists have long recognised that a vast amount of our behaviour is driven by processes that operate below the level of our conscious awareness. So simply asking people why they behave the way they do or what they intend to do in the future is very poorly predictive: if you are not conscious of the factors that influence you, how can you introspect and comment on them? FMRI, however, allows us to identify, measure and understand how many of these influences operate on our unconscious perception, helping us to predict what people are going to do, based on what is going on in their brain at the time they were scanned.

For example, Dr Adrian Owen and his team at Cambridge University found that they were able to predict which of numerous abstract images would be subsequently remembered by their participants, based on the amount of activity observed in the hippocampus (a structure involved in encoding memories) at the time they were shown each image, while in the scanner. This held true despite the fact that the participants were certain they would not be able to recall which images they had or had not previously seen. In a more applied FMRI experiment, Professor Brian Knutson in California showed that the way individuals' brains responded to products shown in the scanner was a better predictor of what they would subsequently purchase than what the subjects said they would buy at the time. But how is all this relevant to helping save the planet?

Brain imaging technologies such as FMRI are being used not only to predict how people will behave in the future, but also to evaluate the relative efficacy of different messages aimed at effecting behavioural change. For example, in a recent commercial study of the effects of cigarette warning labels on smokers' propensity to smoke, bleak black and white notices that 'Smoking Kills' or 'Smoking harms your unborn baby' had no more effect on suppressing the brain's nicotine craving site (the *nucleus accumbens*) than viewing cigarette packs without warnings.

Imaging studies like this confirm what neuroscientists already suspected – simply telling people to change their habits does not work. So what does? It turns out that a great deal of our everyday behaviour comprises a series of well-learned automated behaviours such as making the tea or coffee, bathing, driving to work, choosing the foods we eat and the things we buy. These habitual behaviours are distinct from the goal-directed behaviours that we perform when learning new things such as HOW to drive the car, WHY caffeine is rewarding in the morning and WHAT marmalade we find most palatable. We call these goal-directed because they are actions performed in order to achieve a specific goal (eg working to obtain a reward or learning how to avoid pain).

Importantly, a key feature of goal-directed behaviour is that it puts us into a state that make us amenable to change in a way that habitual or automated behaviours do not. So can we harness this knowledge to make people change their bad habits in favour of behaviours that are less harmful to the planet? By asking people consciously to focus their attention on the original goals that underpinned the development of a habitual behaviour, we typically become conscious of the factors that have led to our actions and also to consider alternative options. In this goal-directed mode, communications that deliver reasoned arguments about how a consciously identified goal might be better attained, with expectations about what to expect from a new behaviour (and subsequent delivery of that experience), provide a mechanism by which we can begin to effect behavioural change.

But it is not just the health of the planet that is at stake, it is also the individuals that live on it. Mental illnesses such as schizophrenia, manic-depression and numerous personality disorders affect hundreds of millions of people worldwide. But diagnosis of these crippling illnesses relies on self-report of symptoms rather than any objective neurological assessment. How then can we begin to understand these disorders unless we can peer into the brains of those so afflicted?

Functional imaging techniques have made remarkable inroads into the neural bases of many of these diseases – providing physiological evidence of how auditory hallucinations are manifest, of the brain structures implicated in delusions and the neural basis of thought disorders. Such insights are significantly aiding the development of more effective drug treatments and behavioural interventions – as well an improved understanding of the nature of the patient's experience.

So does all this amount to the ability to talk directly to the human brain? In an astounding paper published in the journal *Science*, Dr Adrian Owen demonstrated how patients with 'locked-in syndrome' (unable to speak, move or initiate any self-generated action whatsoever) have found a route by which to communicate with the outside world – directly via their brains. Unable to generate a response and therefore with no means by which to evaluate to what extent the patient was conscious of the outside world, Dr Owen and his team started scanning patients with this condition using FMRI and asking them a series of questions that would require a Yes or No answer. Given that different parts of the brain are involved in different tasks, they asked patients to imagine playing tennis if they wanted to respond 'No' to a question, or instead to imagine walking around the inside of their homes if they wished to reply 'Yes'. Remarkably, some of these patients had clearly heard and understood the instructions and were able to give accurate answers to questions of an autobiographical nature.

The implications of this research are manifold. In addition to giving hope to those for whom communication with the outside world seemed lost, the findings from this and studies like it are beginning to provide important insights for the field of neural prosthetics. These devices, designed to be planted in the brain to recover the functions lost through brain injury, hold the very real promise to help the mute speak, the blind see and the lame walk. I for one, think that is certainly something to be optimistic about.

Cognition and intelligence – peering into the 'black box'

Jackie Chappell

In the Pixar film of the same name, WALL-E the robot is programmed to collect, compact and stack rubbish, which he does very efficiently. However, he also shows curiosity and playfulness, exploring the function of the lever on a fire extinguisher, discovering that you can pretend a car hub cap is a hat and solving the knotty problem of how to classify a 'spork' when you have existing collections of spoons and forks. Why do we not yet have any robots capable of the kind of flexible intelligence necessary to make decisions about novel objects, explore their environment and show curiosity about surprising things?

There are certainly formidable technological challenges, but the main problem is that we just do not understand intelligence sufficiently. What is intelligence, and why do some animals (like humans, other apes, crows, parrots and even octopuses) invest heavily in the neural 'hardware' required, while others do not? That sounds pessimistic, but I am hopeful that we are at least getting closer to clarifying the question, if not the answer.

Understanding intelligent behaviour (cognition) seems to be an intractable problem. We all think that we know it when we see it, but defining exactly what it is, elucidating the mechanisms behind it and building artificial systems to replicate it all seem to be much more difficult than we once thought. One problem is that cognition is a very complex phenomenon, spanning multiple levels of organisation from molecular processes in the brain to the overt behaviour of the animal, and some aspects are inaccessible to direct investigation.

Evolution is an important part of the puzzle too. Big brains are expensive organs to build and maintain, so we have to assume that there is something special about animal brains – that computers still lack – that favoured their evolution despite their biological costs. We need to learn more about what brains are used for. What exactly are the functions of visual perception, curiosity, play and exploration in animals, and what benefits do they bring?

Finally, the environment that the young, developing animal finds itself in can also have a significant impact on its intelligence. We know from experiments on a variety of non-human animals (and tragic cases of neglect in humans) that growing up in an enriched or an impoverished environment can have a lasting effect on behaviour. By studying the environments and their demands together with robotics and artificial intelligence (AI), researchers have begun to ask new questions about how various kinds of environmental complexity relate to cognitive mechanisms and learning processes. I am confident that working harder on clarifying the questions will lead us towards new answers.

Whilst understanding natural intelligence might help us to build better robots, the reverse is also true: one of the best ways to increase your understanding of a system is to try to build one, so in trying to construct intelligent machines, we may come to understand more about intelligent animals. This viewpoint can also help us understand the adaptive function of intelligence. By analysing an animal's environment from the perspective of a robot designer, we can conduct a 'requirements analysis' for that species. This takes into account the opportunities that the environment provides and the constraints and problems it imposes, as well as the animal's needs and functions.

Robotics and AI research is useful to biologists in other ways. Animals have rich and complex behaviour, but we know very little about the mechanisms underpinning that behaviour, whereas artificially intelligent systems currently have relatively few competences, but because we designed the system, we know all about the mechanisms involved. This means that we can use artificial systems to model and test hypotheses about parts of the natural system, and observe the effects of altering the mechanisms in ways that we simply cannot do with natural systems.

Ultimately, cognition requires brain mechanisms, and recent scientific and technological advances in neurobiology and psychology have opened promising lines of enquiry. Functional magnetic resonance imaging (FMRI) is a non-invasive technique which allows us to see which regions of the brain become activated when people are actively engaged in solving problems. The technology is improving all the time, with novel techniques and better spatial and temporal resolution of the images, and we may soon be able to study awake, moving animals undertaking more naturalistic tasks.

Potentially, this allows us to peer into the 'black box' of the brain while it is running, and relate internal neural activity to both external behaviour and hypothesised cognitive mechanisms. However, in order to understand the processes involved, we still need to determine the function of those brain regions, and the ways in which they relate to one another and interact. In addition, we need to understand the evolutionary function and developmental trajectory of the behaviour in order to interpret fully the results of these new technologies.

Despite all the technological advancements, there is still a vital role for low-technology behavioural experiments. Elegant, carefully controlled experiments in semi-natural conditions can reveal astounding and unexpected cognitive abilities in animals. There has been a steady stream of findings showing that various non-human animals have abilities previously thought to be unique to humans. By administering a battery of different kinds of tests, we can, for example, begin to distinguish between learning governed by rather rigidly applied rules and that based on more abstract and flexibly applied concepts. This can be further refined by collaborating with robotics and AI researchers to build and test models of some of the component systems.

The broad field of cognitive science has grown enormously in the last decade, benefiting from these kinds of cross-disciplinary collaboration and improvements in technology. By combining all of these approaches and attacking the problem on multiple fronts, and by learning from advances in other fields, will we make progress. Perhaps then I can have my own personal WALL-E, as well as gaining a deeper understanding of human cognitive abilities and those of crows, parrots and apes.

Understanding incentives – governments and carbon emissions

Richard Green

I am writing as an economist who has been studying the electricity industry for 20 years – since shortly before it was privatised and competition was introduced to the industry in the UK. If there is one single belief that unites economists, it is that people and organisations respond to the incentives that they face – they will tend to make choices which they believe will produce better outcomes than the alternatives. Understanding this may be the key to solving one of our most pressing problems: carbon emissions.

When we think about behaviour and incentives, we should go beyond the purely 'economic' factors. Drink-driving has declined in the UK, perhaps because stronger enforcement has changed the risk–benefit calculation ('What is the pleasure I get from this drink, versus the probability and cost of losing my licence?'), but also because social attitudes to it have changed. It may be that in future social attitudes will hold some forms of carbon-intensive behaviour to be equally unacceptable. That would probably be for the long term, however, and countries like the UK need to be cutting their carbon emissions quite sharply now if we are to limit the probability of excessive climate change.

One way to impose such a change is to make a new rule (and enforce it), but what should that rule be? We know about many ways to reduce emissions, but we do not know what all of them will actually cost, and we can be confident that we will develop other solutions which few people have thought of yet. How could a government create a set of rules that would lead us to adopt what turn out to be the best solutions? To an economist, creating a suitable incentive is usually far better than making a hard and fast rule. This is particularly true when most carbon emissions are bound up with our choices of what to consume and how to produce it – the core issues of economics.

Some incentives can be positive – we can be rewarded for doing things that reduce carbon emissions. Home insulation, renewable energy and public transport are subsidised in various ways. Biofuels are taxed less heavily than petrol and diesel. But relying solely on positive incentives would be too expensive, and we will need to use the negative incentive of making carbon emissions more expensive to those that cause them.

There are two main ways of doing this. The traditional method of reducing demand for something is to tax it. In most cases, the reduction in demand is seen as a bad thing (people are not making the same choices that they would have made if the government had not had to raise revenue). In the case of a product that causes problems, however, such as alcohol or tobacco, reducing demand is seen as a benefit of high taxation. A carbon tax (which would actually be levied on the carbon-containing fuel, rather than by measuring the carbon dioxide when it is emitted) would make carbon emissions more expensive and give companies an incentive to reduce them. It need not lead to an increase in the overall level of taxation because the proceeds from a carbon tax could be used to reduce taxes on things that the government wanted to encourage, like work (income tax).

But few governments have chosen to use carbon taxes. A more recent alternative, carbon trading, has proved much more popular. With an emissions trading scheme, companies must either surrender a permit for every tonne of carbon dioxide they emit or make a payment into a buy-out fund. Governments running the scheme issue the permits, either giving them away to companies likely to need them or selling them. If the volume of emissions in the absence of the scheme would be greater than the number of permits issued, then those permits become scarce, and hence valuable.

Companies can choose to continue emitting and either buy permits or hang on to those they were given, but this involves a cost. In the case of a company that was given permits, this is the so-called opportunity cost of giving up the chance to earn money by selling them – something that may not appear in the company accounts but is a genuine cost to an economist. Some companies will find ways of cutting emissions that are cheaper than the cost of buying (or not selling) permits. Once enough companies do this, the demand for permits (the emissions that companies want to make) will just equal the number of permits issued (the emissions that the government is willing to allow). The emissions target should be met, and the price of the permit should be equal to the cost of the most expensive techniques needed to achieve this.

That permit price then gives us valuable information – what other companies are willing to pay to avoid reducing their carbon emissions. Any company can then look at its own options, estimate their costs and decide which of them are worth putting into practice. If it is more profitable to do something that will reduce emissions and sell spare permits rather than to continue with business as usual, this implies that the company has a relatively low cost of abatement. If the company's cost of abatement is relatively high, then it will be cheaper to buy permits, allowing others with better options to reduce their emissions instead. In either case, the overall target should be met.

The great advantage of using tradable permits is that the reductions should be made by the companies that can do so most easily, without using a bureaucracy of regulators to establish which those companies are. The bureaucracy will be expensive, and it will probably get the wrong answer. Trading schemes have been shown in practice to deliver emissions reductions relatively cheaply.

The US used a tradable permit scheme to reduce sulphur emissions from power stations, and it has been estimated that trading reduced the cost of doing so by 57% compared with a rule-based approach. Furthermore, the out-turn permit price was less than half the level predicted by analysts before the scheme started – in other words, given the right incentives, companies found cheaper ways to reduce their emissions.

The European Union's Emissions Trading Scheme has been criticised because the price of permits fell dramatically during 2006, when the first data on actual emissions were released. These turned out to be so close to the number of permits issued that the permits were unlikely to be scarce, and their price fell accordingly. In the first 17 months of the scheme, however, when the prices were high, it did lead to emissions reductions. One estimate puts these between 50 and 100 million tonnes, or up to 5% of the 2 billion tonnes of actual emissions by the installations affected by the scheme. Most of this probably came from switching from coal to gas in the power sector, which is responsible for nearly three-quarters of the emissions covered by the Scheme.

It is true that many electricity companies in Europe have benefited from the Emissions Trading Scheme because the price of permits has raised the price of power, even though the companies were given many of the permits they need. These windfall profits can be seen as a disadvantage of the way the Scheme was implemented. The problem is not that the price of electricity rose but that governments gave away valuable emissions permits for nothing. In future, generators will have to buy their permits and carbon-intensive generators will no longer make windfall profits. Generators with low carbon emissions will make more money in a world with an emissions trading scheme, which is desirable because it raises the incentive to invest in low-carbon power.

We know that emissions trading, and other economic incentive schemes, can lead to reduced levels of pollution. Some reductions can be made through short-term operating decisions, such as burning gas rather than coal. But really large reductions will require investment and companies will only be willing to make these if they believe that the incentives will be maintained for a long period. That requires strong political commitment and perhaps international agreement.

The aim of this contribution is to show that if governments create the right incentives, people and companies will respond and reduce their carbon emissions. Will governments around the world actually create those incentives? The jury is still out.

Crop protection – science and citizenship

David Chandler

Optimism is based on a philosophy that we are living in the best of all possible worlds, and that good will necessarily triumph over evil. At this point, I have to put my hands up and say that I am not an optimist. I struggle to understand people who have an inherent faith that 'things will work out for the best'. My scientific education – with its emphasis on critical thought and analysis – together with my life experiences, tells me that this is not how the world works.

This is not to say that I am a pessimist. And, as an aside, I can imagine that an overwhelming faith that the good times are just around the corner used to have a selective advantage. It would have been the optimistic cavemen who went out to bring home woolly mammoth for dinner, not considering for an instant the high probability of being squashed to death by seven tonnes of fur, feet, trunk and tusk. The pessimistic cavemen would have stayed at home … and starved. My argument is that, in our modern world, optimism is not enough.

I work as a biologist in crop protection. I love my work, but it is not prestigious. Indeed, until recently crop protection was treated as a scientific backwater and suffered from years of underinvestment. You think science is glamorous? Try going to a dinner party and telling people that you conduct research into better ways of controlling caterpillars. Then sit back and watch the tumbleweed blow down the hall.

Anyway, with my unglamorous biologist's hat firmly on my head, here is some information for all you optimists out there. Our planet is undergoing its sixth mass extinction of animal, plant and microbial life. What is causing it? Take a wild guess. So, goodbye polar bear, goodbye honeybee, goodbye unassuming soil fungus that just might be producing the next cure for cancer as one of its secondary metabolites. And do not forget that the climate is changing, it is getting warmer, sea levels are rising and the oceans are becoming acidic.

Oh, did I also mention that we have to double food production by 2050 in order to feed our rapidly expanding human population? The trouble is, we are already using an awful lot of Earth's fertile land to grow food. And the latest research indicates that we need to put at least one-third of our land area over to nature conservation if we want to protect biodiversity and continue to receive ecosystem products, such as breathable air and clean water. Yes, we really, really, really need the biodiversity that we are so busy sending to its doom. It reminds me of the Gary Larson cartoon of the Dinosaur Convention. The chief dinosaur stands at the podium and says: 'The future's bleak, gentlemen. The earth's climate is changing, the mammals are taking over, and we each have a brain the size of a walnut.'

Still feeling optimistic?

No doubt there will be other articles in this collection that will tell you about the amazing breakthroughs happening now in science that are giving us new insights into nature. They will write about new advances in medicine and technology that will improve our lives. They will inform you about the advances in genomics and systems biology that are revealing the true complexity of living things, and reinforcing our knowledge of the interconnectedness of all life on earth. They will tell you that science is an infinitely deep activity that advances our culture and humanity. All this is true. And yet for each new drug discovery, and for each new exquisite mathematical theorem, we all know that someone out there is using science to develop a chemical weapon or cluster bomb, or is planning a way to pump even more carbon into the atmosphere.

If history tells us anything, it tells us that our capacity for scientific discovery and invention runs far ahead of our ability to use knowledge and technology wisely. It tells us that people will subjugate science and technology for base purposes: to achieve dominance over others, to accumulate material wealth at the expense of natural capital and well-being, to harm our fellow human beings.

And yet I sense a change. This comes not from optimism, but from realism. Here are some truths that most people now hold to be self-evident:
- We cannot continue to base human life on the mass consumption of non-renewable resources. We must develop sustainable systems for providing our food, clothing and water.
- We must reverse human-induced climate change.
- We must protect biodiversity.

And in order to achieve these things, we must couple science and technology with morality, justice and equity.

Things are happening now that means sustainable living is a realistic goal. Governments are starting to put money into sustainable futures. Even my own scientific backwater, crop protection, is starting to be recognised as a key area. And if you do not believe me, consider this. About 40% of the potential global crop yield is lost to pests, diseases and weeds. Another 20% is destroyed post harvest. Thus, improving our ability to protect our crops is a highly significant way for increasing access to food and freeing up land for nature conservation.

If we can reduce waste further down the food supply chain, then we are onto a real winner. In the UK, we throw away about one-third of the food we buy from the supermarket, often because it runs past its best-before date. Meanwhile, our retailers reject much of the fresh produce supplied by farmers and growers simply because it does not meet their stringent standards for cosmetic appearance. Reducing waste in the food chain is a realistic, achievable way of living more sustainably.

The way we view science is also changing for the better. Science used to be managed, run and viewed as if it were outside of civil society. There was little dialogue between scientists and the public. Science communication policy was centred on 'the public understanding of science', as if ordinary citizens had neither the capacity nor the right to comment on, and influence, the kind of science being funded by the government or private industry. Now the onus is on scientists as citizens, with active engagement between interested parties, to develop science for the common good and to discuss the role of science in our modern culture. Pioneering programmes are being set up, such as the UK Rural Economy and Land Use initiative, which funds collaborative research between social and natural scientists to address pressing issues in agriculture and the environment in holistic ways. This new-found social maturity in our science marks a major step forwards.

We now live in an age in which our actions have global consequences. We are starting to realise just how deeply we are connected to each other and to the natural world. We are capable of combining our ingenuity and flair for science with basic values of the common good, and thereby take our planet out of peril. We humans are nothing if not adaptable, and it can happen faster than you might expect. This is a time for realists, not optimists.

If history tells us anything, it tells us that our capacity for scientific discovery and invention runs far ahead of our ability to use knowledge and technology wisely.

We are capable of combining our ingenuity and flair for science with basic values of the common good.

Forensic linguistics – advancing justice

Tim Grant

I am optimistic about the contribution of social science to the delivery of justice. We are all perhaps more familiar with the contribution of hard sciences to forensic investigation. In particular, the invention and development of DNA profiling has revolutionised criminal investigation, both in bringing prosecutions and in acquitting the convicted innocent. Popular culture recognises this contribution in many TV dramas. According to the same TV dramas, the contribution of social scientists might seem best to be made by criminal psychological profilers whose incisive input resolves cases where traditional, slow-witted policing has failed.

But in real policing, linguists are joining psychologists in the role of investigative advisor. Forensic linguists examine threats, harassing emails and other communications, helping the police (or defence teams) identify the writers. I am confident that such linguistic and psychological advice can be valuable in helping to deliver justice, but the impact is naturally limited to a small number of exceptional cases. My greater optimism springs not from the impressive but limited contribution made by these profilers, but from the more widespread application of social science findings to the development of expertise in the investigative interviewing of suspects and witnesses.

Research into investigative interviewing arose out of a number of high-profile miscarriages of justice, including cases such as the Birmingham pub bombings of 1974. In this case six men were convicted of causing the explosions which killed 21 people and injured 182. Under intensive and allegedly violent police interrogation, two of the men produced statements which were taken to be confessions. On the basis of these confessions, the six men were convicted. In 1991, at their third appeal, evidence was heard which discredited both the confession evidence and the forensic evidence against the men and the convictions of the Birmingham Six were quashed.

Psychological interest in interrogation demonstrates clearly that producing false confession does not require violence, that under certain pressures we are all vulnerable to confessing falsely and also that there exist particularly vulnerable individuals who may produce false confession in response to apparently innocuous questioning.

Social science research into police interactions with suspects and witnesses is not restricted into how and when false confessions will be produced. There is also considerable work on how to elicit maximum good information from the memories of witnesses. The danger here is that memory is incredibly fragile and even the competent, co-operative witness is likely to provide false information if not questioned carefully. Psychological and linguistic research in this area has shown how good questioning can produce reliable results and that even children and vulnerable adults can provide dependable evidence of their experiences.

What I find extraordinarily encouraging is that the police and criminal justice system in the UK has engaged fully with this social science research agenda and has invested heavily to change law, policy and practice. The

Police and Criminal Evidence Act 1984 marked a turning point. Since then we have learnt how to interview suspects effectively but without coercion and how to interview ordinary witnesses to best effect. But perhaps most importantly, we have learned how to interview children and vulnerable adults, thereby giving them access to the justice system which should be protecting them.

In this substantial change to the delivery of justice in England and Wales we have moved from 'police interrogation' to 'police interview' for suspects and witnesses. Credible claims are made that since 1990 there has not been a miscarriage of justice in the UK based on a coerced confession. With regard to witnesses, we recently saw a rapist convicted based on the courtroom evidence of a girl, aged four, who was just two years old when she was abused and interviewed.

The UK model is now being exported. In jurisdictions such as Australia, where UK police training in interviewing competes with models based on the interrogation of suspects, the UK method is sometimes referred to as the 'British-Ethical' model of interviewing. This is something of which we can be justifiably proud.

The narrower contribution of social science research to the delivery of justice in individual cases can be just as impressive. As with some of the psychological input into the delivery of justice, forensic linguistics originated with work on false confession and miscarriage of justice. Linguists can sometimes say that the claims made in court of a particular document are unlikely to be true. Well-known examples include linguistic analyses of the confession statement of Timothy Evans, convicted of the murder of his wife and child in 1950; of Derek Bentley, convicted of murdering a police officer in 1952; and of Patrick Molloy, convicted of playing a part in the murder of newspaper boy Carl Bridgewater in 1978.

In each of these cases the convictions were eventually quashed by the Court of Appeal. Before routine tape recording, the normal interview process would have been to produce a transcript of the interview and on the basis of an interview or the transcript to write the witness statement. One example of the power of language evidence is that in the Bridgewater case, Malcolm Coulthard was able to demonstrate that it was most likely that Molloy's interview transcript was in fact based on the text of the witness statement. That is to say, these two documents had been produced in the wrong order. This language analysis, suggesting that there was something seriously awry with the statements, contributed to the appeal process.

As well as examining statements produced through police interviews, linguists also analyse written material of interest to investigators. One task we engage in is to comment on the meaning of unusual words or phrases, such as those which occur in the slang or patois used by gangs. For example, it may be important to know whether it is a threat to write that you will 'bore', 'juk' or 'duppy' another person. Each of these verbs does indeed indicate a threat and all of them derive from Caribbean English. The first two convey a threat to stab and the last one to kill, and they all appeared in cases involving mobile phone text messages and internet relay chats.

It is not the role of the linguist to evaluate the degree of threat or risk, although this may be done by a psychologist, but the linguist can sometimes identify whether the writer's first language is English, perhaps what their educational or social background is and sometimes whether they are a man or a woman. Language varies in predictable ways across social groups and by understanding this variation we are sometimes able to locate the social origins of a particular text.

However, the most common investigative task faced by linguists at the Centre for Forensic Linguistics is comparative authorship analysis. In these cases we are asked to determine whether a text message or email was sent by a person accused of some crime or other wrongdoing. In one recent case a suicide note was found to have been written in a distinctive style which was consistent with the writing of a suspect rather than the dead man.

Justice is delivered – indeed it is constructed – daily in our courts, with gains and set-backs and recoveries. The legal quest for truth and for justice depends upon good evidence to assist the courts in decision-making, but also on good understanding of the processes which influence the decisions made. My optimism springs from the fact that this delivery of justice has already been improved by the contribution of the social sciences,

changing behaviour

both in the provision of evidence and in the reform of processes – and there is the prospect of many more contributions.

PART 4

The ways of science

CHAPTER 7

Working together

Translational research – on the brink of a major revolution

Helen Maddock

n Britain and worldwide there is an emerging area of science known as 'Translational Medicine' which encompasses a multidisciplinary approach, applying basic and clinical science knowledge and skills to topics including disease diagnosis and treatment, experimental study design and regulatory procedures. Translational medicine also covers relevant technical biomedical innovations, as well as both clinical trials and health-outcomes research. Translational medicine integrates a wide range of subjects to enable the translation between basic and medical science, in order to enable well-needed developments in the diagnosis and treatment of patients and also possibly the prevention of disease development.

For the speciality of translational medicine to evolve it is extremely important that clinical researchers, translational researchers and basic researchers collaborate in order to produce a detailed clinically relevant research strategy, and obviously this is multifactoral. Bridging the divide that separates laboratory biomedical research from improvements at the clinic has always been difficult. Now, translational research has emerged as a field in its own right, aided greatly by the Medical Research Council (MRC) with a collection of initiatives that prioritise efforts to shepherd biomedical discoveries into clinical application and the establishment of six new translational medicine centres in the UK.

As translational research has gained momentum, training opportunities in the field have expanded rapidly. With funding bodies such as the MRC actively encouraging the area of translational medicine, I am optimistic that this new discipline will develop into a well-recognised and rewarding branch of science. I am extremely hopeful that within the UK and worldwide scientists, clinicians, researchers and stakeholders (industry, society, state, health systems) are beginning to evolve and work together to ensure adequate undergraduate and postgraduate education encompassing new strategies of clinical and translational research for individuals to have the relevant knowledge to ensure success in the drug discovery and clinical arena.

There is a great need for the strengthening and rebuilding of physiology and pharmacology to bridge the gap between the laboratory and the whole organism and correlate early markers of safety and benefit with actual outcomes in patients. The breaking down of artificial organisational barriers and aiding the advancement of interdisciplinary translational science is still in its early days and will inevitably facilitate the understanding, improvement and treatment of disorders and diseases.

The mapping of the human genome has already had a profound effect on the future of the health industry. Science is on the brink of generating a major revolution in medicine, thanks to advances in '-omics', including genomics, transcriptomics, proteomics, metabolomics, metabonomics and pharmacogenomics. We are currently undertaking translational research to develop a novel and innovative process and assay to profile the activity of drugs on the heart. Research undertaken within my laboratory endeavours to pursue truly medically relevant research projects, with a primary aim to interpret what happens in a clinical setting with respect to disease conditions or drug therapy and translate this into more pre-clinically relevant experiments.

We are currently investigating drug-related cardiovascular complications in conjunction with biomechanical, quantitative pharmacological and biochemical techniques which could provide a new and exciting avenue for both advanced clinical insight and improvement of the drug development process. For example, we are about to initiate a study trying to define pharmacogenomic risk factors for proarrhythmia to tailor cardiac safety to individual patients and investigating pharmacodynamic markers for drugs that increase the risk of atrial fibrillation.

We are also collaborating with cardiologists and cardiothoracic surgeons in undertaking a medical research study into how a heart attack (a lack of blood flow to the heart) results in injury and death of the heart muscle cells in the affected area. This project aims to determine whether certain pharmacological agents are able to reduce the injury caused to the heart muscle cells during a heart attack, as well as helping to develop understanding of the process of injury to the heart during a heart attack. This is an extremely important study that will enable basic science to be translated into clinical science and an excellent example of translational research. There is so much we still do not know about the heart, and this will be one of the first studies of its kind to look at myocardial cell death.

The UK-based pharmaceutical industry has been a major contributor to the dramatic improvement in human health by discovering 15 out of the 75 top medicines used worldwide. This success, and the level of pharmaceutical-industry investment in the UK (£10 million per day), is based on the excellence of UK science. However, the development of new pharmaceuticals is subject to a high level of attrition, which has not improved despite significant advances in technology. The cost of bringing a new drug to market has been estimated to be over $800 million and a substantial proportion of this cost is borne in the pursuit of failed drug candidates. Reducing the level of attrition is therefore one of the most significant challenges facing the pharmaceutical industry.

Associated with the cost of development itself is the time spent in such development. Increasingly, the pharmaceutical industry is keen to identify as early as possible those drug candidates which will not progress successfully through development. Thankfully the industry and those in the medical profession are now realising that it is very dependent on uniting the skills of integrative pharmacologists, translational medical scientists and clinical scientists in order to ensure future successful drug discovery and development. With the growth of this newly emerging area there is demand for a whole new range of suitably trained scientists to speed up the critical task of translating basic laboratory medical research into commercially ready medical biotechnology and drugs for the diagnosis and treatment of patients.

I am confident that the evolving translational approach to science recognises that accurate predictions are based on the quality, reliability and relevance to the disorder of both the pre-clinical and the clinical measures. And I am hopeful that students undertaking biomedical and medical degrees will be trained adequately in the area of translational medicine so that they are able to identify biomarkers that are accessible both pre-clinically and clinically, to bridge the gap between animal and human studies and to facilitate early clinical decision-making.

The further development of novel translational approaches combined with the evolving focus on the '-omics', as well as emphasis on the identification of reliable biomarkers for disorders that correlate with clinical and functional endpoints, provide a fresh and optimistic approach to minimising the risk in drug discovery and development. Basic and clinical scientists in research and within the pharmaceutical industry are embarking on an extremely exciting journey, with an approach which will involve parallel and theoretically linked advances in the pre-clinical and clinical aspects of the drug-discovery process.

Liver disease –
a new spirit of scientific and
clinical collaboration

Deirdre Kelly

I am both a clinician and academic researcher specialising in caring for children with liver disease. My research is divided between clinical research, such as clinical trials of new medication for children or studies of quality of life and outcome, and laboratory-based research using molecular biological and genetic techniques to understand and treat the causes of liver disease in childhood.

I am optimistic that the new emphasis on translational research in the NHS, which began with the introduction of 'Best Research for Best Health' and the establishment of the National Institute of Health Research (NIHR), will completely change how clinicians, scientists and health service managers will think about and undertake research, integrating research and development into daily clinical practice. This initiative, coupled with the introduction and implementation of Academic Health Science Centres across England, will focus the best researchers and scientists and encourage them to build up a critical mass of expertise to consolidate and combine clinical and basic research, and clinical trials – bringing the findings of basic science from the 'bench to the bedside'.

Today, the many different approaches in research methodology required to answer complex questions about mechanisms of disease and/or the genetic basis of disease require sophisticated co-operation between experts and an end to the single laboratory hiding its work from the world until publication of its unique findings. We have learnt to work together, to trust other researchers and ensure their adequate recognition. I am confident that this new more co-operative working in basic science and its implementation in practice will continue, so that we will be empowered and funded to develop basic science together with clinicians, implementing the findings seamlessly for the benefit of our patients.

So how will these initiatives and advances help my own patients? Over the last 20 years, advances in molecular and genetic technology have improved our ability to diagnose and treat rare diseases in children, transforming their lives, and have given us an understanding of both normal and abnormal physiology.

For instance, the team based at Birmingham Children's Hospital and the Department of Molecular Genetics at the University of Birmingham have discovered a number of new genetic defects responsible for some of the devastating diseases in our patients. We have worked together to identify these genes, using sophisticated processes such as genome-wide screening of families who have affected children, and micro array techniques. And we have used our technological skills to develop a 'Gene Chip' so that we can look for many rare genes at once instead of the conventional practice of looking for selective defects one after another. This allows us to make an early, or antenatal, diagnosis and to start appropriate therapy quickly.

The new collaboration between NHS and university science now gives us a vehicle for evaluating the results of our basic science findings in patients, such as finding out how useful the 'Gene Chip' will be in practice, whether families and children really do benefit from a prompt and early diagnosis and whether this is cost-effective. I anticipate that continuing advances in technology will bring in newer and faster methodology to help us answer these questions sooner.

Identifying rare genes is only the first step to understanding disease. Once the gene is identified, we are able to work out what it controls and how it functions in the body, using cell cultures and animal models. This has given us an insight into how different processes within liver (and other) cells work normally and how these processes, if defective, cause disease. It is clear that the further use of this methodology, including the development of better cell lines or culture systems, will be the key not only to understanding disease but also in helping us target future therapy, applying this directly to the affected tissue.

The development of gene therapy has been slow, mainly because of the difficulty in introducing genes into human cells and tissue safely and ensuring that they last long enough to be effective. Recent developments using artificial vectors which are not rejected by the body may be the key to their successful use and I am sure this will be a rapidly expanding area of new research which will be of considerable benefit, not only to my patients but to many others.

I am also optimistic that the recent changes in legislation in both the US and the UK will allow us to harness the potential of stem cell therapy and to develop methodology with either embryonic or induced pluripotential stem cells to treat safely a range of degenerative diseases, not just in the liver but elsewhere. I see this as an essential method of therapy which should halt or prevent much morbidity and mortality in our patients.

In addition, we have seen how effective vaccination has altered outcomes in the developing world with the eradication of smallpox and other previously severe or fatal diseases. Many viral illnesses cannot be prevented by vaccination as yet, but the rapid development of vaccine technology, especially recombinant and DNA vaccines, should be of enormous benefit for many diseases, such as cytomegalovirus, Epstein Barr virus, Hepatitis C and, of course, HIV. So I am certain that future generations will not be at risk from these conditions.

Finally, the rapid development of innovative surgical procedures, supported by the introduction of intensive monitoring and therapy, has meant that complex operations such as liver transplantation have become not only safe but routine. I am confident that we will continue to be innovative in this field, developing robotic or keyhole surgery to minimise harm, whilst nanotechnology will allow us to monitor and support critically ill patients safely. It is even possible that with early diagnosis, effective vaccination and/or the development of gene therapy, stem cell or hepatocyte transplantation we will no longer need to resort to liver transplantation or similar complex surgery.

This new spirit of scientific and clinical collaboration combined with the rapid development of technology encourages us to look to the future with genuine optimism.

Developmental biology –
the need for blue skies research

Elizabeth Oliver-Jones

For the first time in my academic life universities face the prospect of significant reorganisation, which includes both rationalisation of facilities and staffing changes, both scenarios that are unfamiliar territory for tertiary education. The funding levels for responsive mode grants for research council funding have also dropped and the current system can barely support the number of good scientists already within it. This could leave many mid-career scientists, who are often at their most productive, struggling to keep a research profile alive.

Coupled with this, there is an increasing trend to spend what money there is strategically, to maximise perceived impact. In my view this concentration of effort on goal-directed and often applied research is a politically driven short-sighted strategy which fails to recognise that many of the major advances in science are serendipitous and have arisen from blue skies research driven purely on the back of desire for knowledge.

So why against this backdrop should I be optimistic?

From a university perspective this is a great opportunity to put one's house in order; to look carefully and strategically at areas of investment, including both the core tasks of education of students and the research portfolio. A reduction in funds or flat level funding will provide a challenge to many universities, encouraging them to look more carefully at how and where they spend their money to maximise both the educational experience of the student cohort and the effective research of their academic staff. This should ensure that the main purposes of a university, to educate students and carry out research, are carried out professionally, enthusiastically, yet economically.

An important part of this will be the development of new methods to deliver the curriculum in an innovative and efficient manner. And this in turn will enable research-active staff to have the maximum opportunity to fulfil their research potential in an increasingly difficult research environment.

As a developmental biologist working on the vertebrate model organism, *Xenopus laevis*, I am part of a UK community which has been traditionally very strong in the field of developmental biology and more recently in stem cell biology. I am confident that this strength will continue despite the difficulties in core and research funding mentioned above. But we need continued support from government, research councils and charities.

There is a place for some highly directed research strategies in the areas of translational medicine, but we need the freedom to be able to research in areas where there may be no currently perceived potential impact and, more importantly, funding to carry this out. This is an area about which I am less optimistic. Whilst stem cell research has attracted enormous quantities of earmarked funding, other areas of developmental biology are struggling to see where funding will come from.

Research using the *Xenopus* system has established gene expression and function in a number of human diseases, for example, colorectal cancer. It has provided biochemical insight into important oncogenes like BRACA1 and has been used to establish ion channel activity, for example, in Long-QT syndrome. These biomedical examples are in addition to a crucial role played by the amphibian system in establishing mechanisms of signal transduction, cell division and basic concepts of development of vertebrates. It would be a cardinal sin if lack of funding for blue skies research in this area stifled developmental biology in the UK in the future.

Perhaps the greatest cause for optimism comes from the quality and tenacity of the scientific fraternity in universities. The average academic is hard working, highly self motivated, intelligent, goal-directed, persistent, and often self-effacing; many are excellent teachers. It is with the academic community that the greatest grounds for optimism lie. Despite cuts in funding dictated from the university's senior management in response to reduced government funding, and cuts in available research funding, university scientists will always make interesting, valuable and translatable discoveries. In fact, they will do this best if they are left alone to get on with their best science without always having to justify their approach. This is how science has made quantum leaps forward in the past, and no doubt will do so in the future.

So, we must explain our science to politicians and explain why hypothesis-driven science is a good thing but purely strategic, goal-directed research might not come up with the best solutions. In this way we will be able to make sure that the UK science base remains innovative and healthy, which should give us all grounds for optimism.

Experimental immunology – sharing ideas

Graham Anderson

rogress in biomedical science takes many different forms. It can be the formulation of a hypothesis that is testable by experimentation, the publication of novel research findings or the translation of basic experimental models to clinical therapy. As an experimental immunologist, what excites me is that research performed within universities in the UK, such as Birmingham, represents an essential component in the treatment of disease and the improvement of health.

Whilst it is becoming increasingly apparent that it is important for research to have a 'translational slant', what excites and enthuses me the most is that there is still plenty of room for 'blue skies' research. To be able to think of an idea and put it to the test by experimentation is a very creative and satisfying experience, especially if it results in new findings, regardless of the initial predictions! From an immunologist's point of view, maintaining a strong foundation in basic research programmes that are aimed at gaining a better understanding of the processes and mechanisms underpinning the generation of a functional immune system represents a key stage in the generation of new treatments and therapeutics.

Our own research in recent years has focused on how to reduce the complexity of the immune system, which has proved to be a real barrier in understanding immunology in the context of both health and disease. Sometimes a reductionist approach can be useful to identify the importance of particular cell partners and molecules that would be difficult to tease out by performing studies on intact organisms. However, in vitro or 'test-tube' experiments rarely recapitulate the events within intact organs, so there is always a trade-off between reducing complexity and increasing artefacts. We hope that we have achieved the best of both these scenarios, by establishing methods to generate 'designer' lymphoid tissues in the lab. In these experiments, we can reduce cellular diversity by isolating cell types of interest from intact organs, and then re-associate our chosen cell types into three-dimensional aggregates under standardised experimental conditions in the lab. In other words, we can simplify cellular complexity without sacrificing tissue organisation, which is important to normal organ function. Perhaps most excitingly, following on from years of test-tube experiments where we used this approach to map out the requirements for several stages of T-cell development, we have begun to transplant these aggregates back into living animals, to monitor how our designer organs function in an in vivo setting, where communication with other lymphoid tissues is possible. Ultimately, we hope that these approaches may aid in cell-based therapies to restore immune system function.

I think there are two key factors to success in science. First, the provision of environments that bring together scientists where casual meetings and conversations can lead to exciting new directions. From my experience, scientists are sociable people, and relish any opportunity to discuss their findings and share ideas – often the very best ideas come from spontaneous conversations, and so environments that foster such interactions are precious. Secondly, progress in science is totally dependent on new ideas and outlooks, which are sometimes provided by students and younger scientists who are not yet tainted by personal biases!

The establishment of exciting teaching programmes that combine with research areas to enable us to identify and train the research leaders of the future is a key part of maintaining basic research output, and we need to continue to draw from the enthusiasm that undergraduate students have for biomedical science. To be able to harness this enthusiasm, together with the curiosity that they have for science, means we need to continue to engage students at an early stage, and provide the opportunities for them to develop their ideas into experimental plans. This allows us to pass on our own optimism and excitement for our subjects, and in turn learn from fresh ideas and new perspectives.

The investment of effort in establishing and maintaining exciting teaching and research programmes in biomedical science is what has kept me in Birmingham for over 20 years, both as a student and as an academic. I am very confident that the combined success of research and teaching will continue to attract people into scientific careers that will underpin the biomedical research of the future.

Cytokines – the interplay of basic and clinical sciences

Ann Vernallis

I study small proteins called cytokines. When cells secrete cytokines, the cytokines diffuse to neighbouring cells where they can bind to specific cell surface receptors and trigger a response. The exchange of cytokines enables non-immune cells to talk to the immune system, and indeed other non-immune cells. The term cytokines dates from the 1970s and it embraces the observation that all of our cells can talk to the cells of our immune system. This is especially important in fighting viruses since viruses can infect so many cell types, but it is important in other microbial infections as well. Cytokines also play key roles in the initiation, maintenance and resolution of inflammation.

The term cytokines is sometimes used more broadly to refer to all small secreted proteins that cells use to talk to each other, including growth factors, neurotrophic factors and some hormones such as erythropoietin and growth hormone. There are hundreds of cytokines and they are expressed everywhere, including in liver, fat, bone, joints, muscle, blood, skin and brain. They contribute to embryonic development and they help keep tissues in homeostasis so that they stay healthy. Abnormal increases or decreases in cytokine levels are associated with a variety of diseases.

Medical interest in cytokines really took off when anti-TNF (tumour necrosis factor) treatment was developed for rheumatoid arthritis. The idea of blocking TNF came from the relatively simple question of asking which cytokines were at the top of the cytokine hierarchy in cultures of cells derived from inflamed joints. When TNF was reduced, other pro-inflammatory cytokines were reduced as well, suggesting an overall reduction in inflammation in the cultures. Patients with rheumatoid arthritis are known to have elevated levels of TNF, and because anti-TNF drugs reduce those levels, joint swelling and the progression of joint destruction are reduced and patients gain mobility.

However, not all patients respond to the anti-TNF drugs. The heterogeneity in response suggests that in some patients there may be different mechanisms driving the disease process. Such heterogeneity fascinates me. Some of these patients may respond better to the inhibition of cytokines other than TNF, such as IL-1 (interleukin-1) or IL-6. Other patients may require drugs which directly modulate immune or non-immune cells. Over time, better basic science and better clinical trials will refine the diagnosis of rheumatoid arthritis into subgroups according to mechanism. It is the interplay between the basic science and the clinical science which makes the field so gratifying and makes me optimistic about new and better treatments for patients.

In my own laboratory, we have been interested in how antibiotics in the tetracycline class inhibit inflammation. One thinks of antibiotics as just affecting bacteria but they affect the host cells as well. Since inflammation contributes to so many disease states, understanding intracellular signalling in inflammation is important. In our experiments we study macrophages, which are so named because these white blood cells ingest microbes and debris. They also play a key role in inflammation. To mimic an inflammatory state, we treat the macrophages with lipopolysaccharide (LPS), a small molecule made by Gram-negative bacteria which accounts for much of the damage done by the bacteria when we get an infection. Of the tetracyclines we have tested in our assay, minocycline is the most potent, so that is the one we have mostly studied.

In order to study how macrophages respond to LPS in the presence of minocycline, we have used a 'proteomics' approach. Proteomics means that we are interested in studying the entire proteome, the complete set of proteins made by the cells. We can do this by using two-dimensional gels which separate proteins into spots according to both size and charge. The proteins in the spots which have been up or down regulated can then be identified using liquid chromatography-mass spectroscopy. We are trying to look at all changes in the proteome, not just changes in candidate proteins which we think might or should be involved. Although it sounds dull to measure protein levels/modifications going up and down, it is fun to find new targets that would not have appeared at the top of a candidate list.

One of the proteins we see increased by minocycline on its own is the metabolic enzyme aldose reductase. In recent decades most work on aldose reductase has been done by clinicians interested in treatments for diabetic neuropathy and it has only recently been shown to contribute to LPS signalling. We are now eager to try to understand how minocycline regulates this enzyme. Perhaps what is most pleasing about finding new targets for minocycline is that as we start reading about them, we find ourselves reading papers in the fields of our colleagues, covering topics such as infection, ischemia, oxidative stress, cardiovascular disease, diabetes, obesity and neurodegeneration. So from a missing, novel or darker spot on a gel, we have opened up new dialogues with other researchers in the department and elsewhere.

What I most enjoy about modern biology is that just as one needs a detailed knowledge of one's favourite molecule, one also needs a broader understanding of the context in which the molecule functions. I am confident that future biologists will not become narrow in their interests despite the acceleration of scientific publishing in specific fields. Instead, their interests will broaden because the interconnections between fields will become ever more apparent.

Chemistry and DNA – interdisciplinarity and core subjects

Jim Tucker

here is much to be optimistic about at present concerning chemistry, not least in the subject itself as an undergraduate degree, where there are signs that it is undergoing something of a renaissance. A few years ago, chemistry seemed to be in retreat with some high-profile departmental closures. Certain heads of UK universities, who believed that removing a core degree programme such as chemistry from their institutions would strengthen their brand, appeared to have the upper hand. However, it seems that the tide may be turning: recently two institutions reinstigated degree programmes in single honours Chemistry and the number of people taking chemistry degree programmes has risen for the fifth year running, reaching over 4,000 for the first time in more than a decade.

So chemistry as an undergraduate degree appears to be proving its worth. The reasons for this are many, but the government has certainly been successfully lobbied over the past decade through organisations such as the Royal Society of Chemistry (RSC). As a result, the 'Chemistry for Our Future' programme was funded by the Higher Education Funding Council England (HEFCE) to help ensure a sustainable chemical science base within higher education, attract able students from all backgrounds and provide chemical science courses appropriate for students and employers in the twenty-first century. On the back of this, the University of Birmingham has just been chosen to host the National Higher Education Science, Technology, Engineering and Mathematics (STEM) Programme, again funded by HEFCE, with the aim of increasing the number of graduates with skills in across the whole science base.

Chemistry research and chemistry teaching are generally intertwined, in particular, at research-intensive universities; the chemistry academic in his or her office might have the brilliant idea and get the funding, but the research is carried out in the laboratory by members of their research group, the vast majority of whom are trained chemistry graduates. Most undergraduate chemists first experience research through their final year undergraduate projects; many then go on to study for a postgraduate research degree such as a PhD, either at their graduating institution or elsewhere. So a strong undergraduate base means that the foundations are laid for a thriving research base. A strong undergraduate intake in Year 1 of an undergraduate course with good and motivated students cheers up academics no end with the thought that such students could be entering their research groups in a few years time.

So what about the current state of chemistry research in UK universities? The infrastructure has certainly improved in many departments, with investment in laboratories and facilities over the past few years. Here in the West Midlands, the regional development agency, Advantage West Midlands (AWM), has funded the purchase of research equipment for the Universities of Birmingham and Warwick. Recently chemistry research at universities in the UK was given a boost by an international review commissioned by the Engineering and Physical Sciences Research Council (EPSRC, the research council which covers chemistry in its remit), which concluded that its health had improved over the past few years with pockets of world-leading and world-class research throughout the community. Links with industry are growing, for example, with increasing numbers of spin-out companies arising from chemistry-based research.

So what about the type of research that chemistry departments are undertaking? Much cutting-edge research these days is interdisciplinary in nature, which is great news for chemistry. As a central science, chemistry has a vital role to play in the synthesis and study of new materials and it offers a great deal for current global challenges. Very recently, the RSC published a list of priority areas, called the RSC Roadmap, where chemists believed they could have the most impact. Amongst others, these include drugs and therapies, energy conversion and storage, solar energy and diagnostics for human health. My own research discipline, supramolecular chemistry, has a role to play in all these areas and just one example from our present research will help me explain how chemistry can impact on one of them: diagnostics for human health.

Our human genome consists of just over 3 billion DNA base pairs that are distributed over 23 chromosomes. From one end of the genome to the other, the four chemical bases G, A, C and T are distributed in a certain order, and a near-complete sequence was first published in 2003. Of course, there are many notable differences of genetic origin between us all, such as eye colour, height, blood group and susceptibility to certain diseases, etc. These come down to subtle variations in the sequence of the four bases in the genome, with one common type of variation called a single nucleotide polymorphism or SNP (pronounced 'snip').

A SNP is where one base in a sequence is substituted for another, for example, G for a C in the sequence CATGT[G/C]AGGCT. Even though each one of us is roughly 99.9% identical to every other human on the planet, the 0.1% of difference still points to over a million variations in the genomic sequence between one person and another, at an average of one variation every 1,000 bases. In fact, most SNPs tend to cluster in certain regions and whilst many are considered as having no biological effect, some are thought to play an important role in affecting susceptibility to various diseases such as cancer and Alzheimer's, and this is where much current research is being focused.

What and where will this increasing knowledge about our own DNA genome lead to? Well, eventually one can envisage a time when each one of us has the opportunity to get their own unique genome sequenced, including all its variations. Obviously this will have societal implications, but it is clear that personalised medicine and healthcare will become increasingly important over the coming decades. From an optimistic standpoint, this will mean that a person's predisposition to a certain disease should be identified at an early stage when it is readily treatable, and adverse reactions by certain people to normal doses of drugs could become a thing of the past as medicines are made more specific to the individual.

What is the role of chemistry research here in terms of diagnostics? Whilst someone's genome can be sequenced now, it is the variations in an individual that need to be identified quickly and cheaply, and it is difficult to meet these criteria using current methods. In collaboration with other scientists, chemists are investigating different approaches to this problem. My research group's approach is to synthesise DNA in the chemistry lab using non-biological methods. The DNA we make (the probe) contains a fluorescent tag that interacts with a strand of normal DNA (the target) in such a way that fluorescence is turned off when the sequence contains one base at the SNP site and turned on when it contains another. We are now working with colleagues in the School of Cancer Studies at the University of Birmingham to test the scope of our findings.

The work described is just one example of how chemistry can be applied to a current interdisciplinary area of research. However, it is important not to forget that the principles and fundamentals of molecular science remain the same. Interdisciplinary research should not come at the expense of training chemists' hands in techniques and their minds in curiosity and creativity through the traditional rigour and depth of a core science subject. The key to successful teaching and research programmes in science at research-intensive universities is to promote degree programmes in core areas of science, whilst offering an interdisciplinary mix of cutting-edge research topics for students as they get closer to graduation.

Bearing in mind, in particular, the forthcoming financial restraints in the immediate future for higher education, a productive approach would consist of a continued strategic and hands-on approach from government to promote priority subjects, along with increased co-operation between universities in various regions and between different subject disciplines within each institution. Through such activities, I am optimistic that a synergy between the education and training of tomorrow's scientists and universities' own research priorities can be achieved.

Animal disease – linking pure and applied research

Laura Green

ommon diseases such as lameness and mastitis occur at a rate of somewhere around 40 cases per 100 animals every year in farmed animals. I truly wish to improve the health, and hence the quality of life, of these animals by improving the management of these diseases. They have been largely ignored since the 1980s, when the food supply to developed countries became cheap and plentiful. However, I have managed to have a career researching on various endemic production diseases as issues such as animal welfare became topical for political reasons.

We live in global times. Climate change has highlighted the inseparable link between land, water and air; the limited supply of fossil fuels has highlighted competition between using land for food and fuel; predictions on world population size and growth have highlighted the fact that that the need for food, particularly protein, is outstripping production. However, we have learnt that we cannot produce low-cost food at any price, including poor animal health: we now need sustainable supplies that balance food production, waste production, water supply, fuel needs and the global population of humans. We can now promote longevity and therefore the health of farmed animals because it makes them more eco-efficient.

This has led to a new phase in research. Research now has to be useful, and useful science is fundable. There was once a great divide between pure and applied science; the former being highly respectable and the latter rather frowned upon, but tolerated if scientists brought in funds for research. We need pure science for the amazing breakthroughs such as the discovery of the structure of DNA or the formulation of laws of physics, but that is no reason to neglect applied science.

I am an applied scientist because this is what drives me. Part of my optimism comes from the fact that I think that useful science spans the pure-applied boundary and that the scope for collaboration between scientists from many backgrounds is becoming greater. I am confident that quality will continue to increase, so that research itself becomes part of the sustainable activity of the world.

Let us take an example to illustrate the divide between controlled scientific research and reality. Apparently we cannot explain how David Beckham can kick a ball on the trajectory that he does and score a goal. Most of the applied scientific challenges that we face today are as complex as understanding the process that Beckham's brain makes when he kicks that ball. In science, we reduce a complex situation to as simple a hypothesis as possible (reductionism) and then test the hypothesis to see whether we can disprove it. We can break down David Beckham's shot into eyesight and sensory and motor neurones linking ball to eye to foot to ball to goal. This disaggregation might be useful for understanding aspects of a process, but if we reassemble them, can we get the ball into the goal or is there some essence of David missing? I suspect there is. To date we often set out to study one area and determine cause and effect, yet in real life we are all making David Beckham-like decisions every day.

Let us apply this to my area. It is now possible to monitor a dairy cow and know how much milk she has produced and of what quality every day. We can use individual computers around her neck to record how much she has eaten and pedometers to determine how active she has been. Soon we will be able to record whether she is lying down or standing up and who she has had contact with. The volume of data from many sources is overwhelming.

I believe that we are moving towards a future where we are increasingly able to include complexity in our research and put together processes that explain the mechanisms of real life. This means moving from a reductionist approach to research to an assimilatory one. It might involve combining tools in the laboratory with mathematics and statistics and social sciences so that we will be able to assimilate and understand complex processes.

With developments in communication, data capture, storage and processing, it will be possible to address increasingly complex problems. I am confident that this will be excellent – and very useful – science.

Nanotechnology – collaboration is king

Jon Preece

I think there is much to be optimistic about. However, before I come on to that, my feeling needs to be put in context as to what has happened technologically in the last 100 years which has led to the current challenges that we – and future generations – face. Then, we can think about being optimistic about solving these challenges.

The last 100 years has seen an unprecedented rate of change in terms of scientific, technological and medical breakthroughs. One of the most telling signatures of these breakthroughs is the remarkable increase in life expectancy during this period. In the early twentieth century, life expectancy was no more than 40 years, whilst today it is over 70. We owe this incredible feat to three things.

The first is the discovery of pharmaceutical drugs for the treatment of diseases. Fleming, Chain and Florey's discovery of penicillin in 1928 stands out as one of the remarkable achievements of the twentieth century, bringing to an end many deaths from simple bacterial infections and resulting in their Nobel Prize award in 1945.

The second factor is the ingenious instrumentation that has been developed to look inside the human body to detect diseases at earlier and earlier stages, exemplified by the discovery of magnetic resonance imaging by Mansfield and Lautebur in the 1970s, for which they were awarded the Nobel Prize in 2003. Finally, there is the detailed work on uncovering the structure and function of biologically active molecules, which was the subject of the 1937 Nobel Prize to Sir Norman Haworth (a professor at the University of Birmingham) and Paul Karrer for their research into vitamins.

Significant step changes are not just limited to the biological world. In 1903 the Wright brothers flew the first aeroplane. Today (106 years later) in excess of one million people are in the air at any one time! This tremendous advance is due to breakthroughs in the materials science of composites, the physics of aerodynamics and the chemistry of fuels.

However, whilst considering these two fantastic accomplishments of human endeavour we must stop to look at the consequences of them. An almost doubling of life expectancy has meant that the population of the world has risen from about 2 billion at the beginning of the twentieth century to 6 billion now, and is projected to rise to 9 billion in about 25 years. These unprecedented rates of increase in the world population have put an increasing burden on the earth's natural resources, and there is a growing fear that at the current rate of population growth there will not be enough energy, food and water to keep the world running! Professor John Beddington, the UK Government Scientific Advisor has chillingly said:

'Can nine billion people be fed? Can we cope with the demands in the future on water? Can we provide enough energy? ... And can we do all that in 21 years time? That's when these things are going to start hitting in a really big way. We need to act now. We need investment in science and technology. 2030 is not very far away.'

So now back to the question what am I optimistic about? Not much you might think, given the backdrop I have just painted! However, you would be wrong. Despite these immense challenges – the type of which humankind has not seen before in terms of complexity and magnitude – which if left untackled make our current way of life unsustainable, I believe solutions will be found.

The reason I am optimistic is not because I believe any particular area of science will deliver some miraculous advances, although I do believe tremendous advances will take place in areas such as nanotechnology (my research area), biomedical science, energy research and environmental science, which will all contribute to solving the challenges outlined above. My optimism stems from how scientists, medics and engineers from all backgrounds are not afraid to speak to each other, to exchange ideas and concepts, to bring new perspectives on old problems, to work together to create innovative and transformative solutions that will have the potential to solve the pressing and serious problems that the world currently faces. Collaboration is king and significant step-change advances will accrue from an amalgamation of disciplines!

However, scientists and engineers have to go one step further. We have to communicate better with the public. We have to engage the public. We need to excite the public about the science and engineering that we do, and show how we care about providing solutions to the challenges we face. We need to do this as the challenges that lie ahead will not be solved by innovative and transformative science alone, but will need to be coupled with governments at the highest level implementing policy that will see the solutions acted upon.

Policy is driven by the court of public opinion and we need to influence it. The clock is ticking, the optimism needs to be harnessed and change implemented. The stakes are too high not to succeed.

Are we training enough young scientists for the future?

Elizabeth Wellington

My chosen subjects of environmental science and microbiology would seem to be all about pandemics, plagues and concerns related to global climate change. These are not threats but real challenges which many of us have experienced directly. In order to meet these challenges and deal with them now and in the future, we need to be prepared – and this will not happen unless we use our scientific expertise to deal with such problems now. My optimism stems from the growing recognition that no one single discipline can solve such global problems but that the answer lies in the development of interdisciplinary teams of research scientists working together.

For the first time in my career I am beginning to notice the facilitation of collaborations between biologists and physical scientists, ranging from soil physicists to mathematicians and engineers. Research councils are responsible for a significant part of the science research done in the UK and applicants are now actively encouraged to prepare grants that both enable collaborations between scientists at different universities and involve integration of different disciplines. This is particularly welcome in environmental sciences where such wide ranging aspects of a particular problem have to be addressed.

If these types of collaboration are funded, then we have the opportunity to train young environmental biologists with particular specialisms but also with an awareness and understanding of the expertise required in the physical sciences. Some may even be truly interdisciplinary, such as systems biologists, who have valuable skills in modelling biological systems and using these as an aid to understanding molecular processes in the cell as well as addressing aspects of evolutionary biology. We need more of this type of scientist in order to study environmental impacts on global ecosystems, and research councils have responded with four-year PhD grants to cover a first year of training essential to cross disciplines.

It is inspiring to work with these students as they really do represent a newly emerging expertise. These are people who can use skills such as mathematical modelling and are still able to conduct biological experiments and/or have a dialogue with a biologist at the appropriate level for the cutting edge of scientific research.

Unfortunately, few opportunities are available for postdoctoral workers to cross disciplines and although some recent schemes have been introduced to support this, many more are needed. An exciting development is the collaboration between different research councils, such as the one involving environment (NERC) and medicine (MRC). These two unlikely bedfellows are considering the prospect of a joint research programme into the environment and human health, focussing on research into the sources of future disease problems related to climate change.

Are we training enough young scientists for the future? Whilst I am optimistic about the clear interest in environmental challenges and identification by funding authorities of the need for joined-up science, I am very worried about the opportunities for young scientists at the postdoctoral level. We can train PhD students and then encourage them to follow through into postdoctoral research, but we need to think about what follows this and what the career structure for research scientists is like.

I am afraid the answer is that very few opportunities exist for scientists to make a career out of research. Few lectureships are available because a lot of universities are starting to reduce staff, while opportunities in the Civil Service are vanishingly rare following the demise of many environmental/soil-related research institutes. If we are to understand the impacts of a changing environment on terrestrial and aquatic ecosystems and deal with the future health problems associated with these changes, then we must invest in young scientists for the future. UK science has always been cost effective compared to other countries and our young scientists will provide opportunities for innovation in industry. We need their skills.

Thyroid disorders – the power of evidence-based medicine

Jayne Franklyn

As a clinical scientist I am optimistic that we can even further improve care given to our patients. One of the major advances in medical practice in recent years has been the emergence of 'evidence-based' medicine. Gone (or at least going) are the days when personal opinion or anecdote were the major drivers to decision-making in terms of investigation and treatment of common diseases.

Evidence-based medicine has at its foundation high-quality clinical research, often underpinned by systematic reviews (that is, proper assimilation of the existing evidence) and randomised clinical trials, which compare new treatments either with placebo (dummy treatments) in which neither patient nor doctor is aware of the treatment given, or with the treatment that was previously regarded as the best. Assimilation of evidence also relies upon accurate data collection, and whilst the development of electronic systems for patient records brings with it specific concerns, undoubtedly the ability to analyse information about tests, treatments and outcomes from large numbers of people with a particular disorder provides a rapid and efficient means of identifying best clinical practice.

This approach has been a feature of our own research into thyroid disorders. The availability of follow-up information (dating as far back as the 1950s) from people who have had a particular form of treatment for their thyroid disease (radioactive iodine treatment for an overactive thyroid) has led to real advances in our understanding of the long-term effects of the underlying condition and how best to treat it.

Real advances in treatment will also undoubtedly accrue from better understanding of the causes of many common disorders. Many of the most common diseases afflicting the twenty-first-century population of an affluent society are so-called 'polygenic disorders', in other words, those which do not result from a single mutation of our genetic makeup but those which reflect the cumulative effect of apparently minor variations in our genetic code. Again, investigation of large numbers of people with common diseases allows us to determine the relative contribution of these minor variations in DNA structure to risk for conditions such as hypertension, obesity and a wide range of 'autoimmune' diseases such as rheumatoid arthritis, type 1 diabetes and thyroid diseases.

We in the University of Birmingham have been lucky in being able to recruit large numbers of people with thyroid conditions with an autoimmune basis who were prepared to donate samples of DNA for research and therefore allow us to define some of the major players in terms of gene variations driving disease risk. Such research is only possible through collaboration with other large centres and our own contribution to the Wellcome Trust Case Control Collaboration has been an excellent example of how scientists from different centres around the world have combined efforts, applied cutting edge new technologies and begun to define just how much a particular gene variation contributes to susceptibility (or protection) to a particular disease.

This approach to research also helps define just how much 'environment' – what we do to ourselves in terms of dietary intake, exercise, smoking or alcohol consumption – contributes to disease risk. Whilst the results of such studies may appear some way from translation into better diagnosis and treatment of specific diseases, it is only via proper understanding of disease causation that we can begin to target resources for disease prevention and therapy.

So whilst advances in information technology and DNA technology may, at first glance, appear distant from the application of clinical research to new developments in diagnosis and treatment, I am optimistic that by harnessing the power of these technologies we can really advance patient care.

Systems biology –
a new way of thinking

Miriam Gifford

I am excited about the new technological advancements sweeping biology – new genomes are being sequenced every day. I am also excited about the discoveries that stem from these developments: identification of key causative genes implicated in controlling disease resistance and environmental perception. However, what I am really optimistic about is a critical component to all of these systems: a whole new way of thinking.

This new way of thinking can enable us to be bold and to attack big problems. The traditional way to tackle a complicated issue is to be reductionist, break it up into bite-size questions to be parcelled out to students or post-doctoral researchers. But this approach distorts or loses the big picture. Better instead to use a method to understand the whole, enabling each individual finding to be connected and understood in a wider context. This new way of thinking can infiltrate many different disciplines at once. In fact, this is both one of its core strengths and also what is actually driving the method itself. So what is this dynamic way of thinking? It is a systems approach.

The definition of systems thinking, most commonly associated with systems biology, can be hard to pin down. Its essence is the development of an iterative cycle of generating biological data (usually on a large scale), integrating that data to build a model or hypothesis to address the question at hand, then designing experiments to test the hypothesis. The results feed back to modify the hypothesis itself, starting a new round of experimentation. Each time the cycle runs, our models aim to come closer to what actually happens in nature.

The systems approach is multifactorial, designed to understand not just how a few genes are connected but how whole networks and processes are integrated into cells, tissues, organisms, populations and ecosystems. Put together, the principle is that investigating the component parts in the context of their relationships with each other helps us understand far more about the parts themselves.

The great power of data modelling is that it can integrate and consider many different types of information that viewed in isolation are much less informative. We can include things that we are confident about – knowns or 'priors' (gene a represses gene b); things we are not sure about – known unknowns (pathogen attack somehow changes flowering time); and things we are not even aware of but that could be important – 'hidden states', biology's unknown unknowns! This type of modelling is not about simply representing some findings, it is about the discovery of new principles.

Systems thinking is not a section of biology, rather it is an approach to the study of biology. It includes everyone: mathematicians, statisticians, engineers, physicists and chemists, as well as biologists; all factor in its delivery. In a chaotic world this flexibility and blurring of traditional boundaries is something that really seems to appeal to today's students. We are beginning to capture this enthusiasm and capitalise on it to train a new generation of scientists.

Researchers who are currently using systems thinking probably studied only in one subject, for example statistics or plant biology. Thankfully this does not stop them from developing new skills in order to understand a new integrative discipline. But what we really need to drive things forward are people who have developed a sort of bilingual or multilingual scientific ability from the start – in other words, the new students. Quite selfishly I want more people with these skills to draw upon in my own research programme!

In order to equip these new students and enable them to take a systems approach to biology, we need to change the way that they are taught. This involves making two quite small but important changes. The first is learning how to analyse biological problems. At the core of this there should be a more complete unification in the teaching of theoretical and practical classes. As well as relevant hands-on experience, students need to be trained in reasoning skills, enabling them to read scientific papers critically. This shifts the emphasis away from simply memorising facts and figures onto marshalling the facts into hypotheses, thinking about biological processes and the experimental approaches that are used to unravel them, and the interpretation of results.

Also critical is the integration of computational methods in the biology syllabus. The current generation of biology students has a high degree of computer literacy but this is not harnessed into their studies. We should not aim to turn biologists into computer scientists, or vice versa, but to train each student in techniques that will enable them to make informed decisions about analysing their own data. This approach would also serve to show computational researchers how their skills might be applied to tackle biological problems.

It is really is exciting to see that in universities up and down the county interdisciplinary learning is feeding into interdisciplinary research and pushing it further. The next challenge is to find a way of linking this with the more rigid structures of undergraduate teaching. The answer here again might be the students themselves, who increasingly want a more active role in directing their own education.

In an age of increasing fees and consequent awareness of the price of education, we could capitalise on the desire of universities for improved student-centricity in order to recontexulatise subjects. The aim would not be to throw out all old ideas and all old subjects but to imbue their teaching with elements of systems thinking. At its simplest this would involve students reinterpreting what is already known in a wider context, asking if this makes sense or if there are elements missing, thinking about what new experiments could be carried out to test these hypotheses – understanding how biology is actually connected. Essentially it involves more – as well as new – thinking.

Today's world faces serious biological problems such as ensuring food security and tacking environmental change, but moving forward we can feel positive about the new modes of thought developing – and trust to our ingenuity to meet the challenge.

Thinking probabilistically - the absurdity of certainty

Ian Nabney

'Doubt is not a pleasant condition, but certainty is absurd.'

Voltaire

Science is all about precision: measuring as accurately as possible and making exact predictions based on theoretical models. Newton's theories of gravitation and dynamics predict the orbit of the moon to within six millimetres every year. So what can science have to say about the complexities and uncertainties of our daily lives, or when a problem is too complicated to build a theoretical model?

The basic answer to this question has been known for centuries: probability theory enables us to work with uncertainty. Since the 1950s, the Bayesian view, that probability can be viewed as our degree of belief in an event, has expanded the applicability of probability from simply counting the frequency of repeated events (such as experimental results or gambling games like dice or cards) to all sorts of propositions. For example, we can talk of the probability that a particular person has angina. This is not a repeated event since the person either does have angina or does not. The probability describes how strongly we believe that they are ill: a value near 1 means that we are pretty sure that they have angina, whilst a value near 0 means that we think it very unlikely. In other words, probability and logic can be combined to make rational predictions in uncertain environments.

This is all very well, but it sounds a bit impractical. In the real world, we have to make decisions, yet how can we do that when our predictions are uncertain? Should we just give up on reason and toss a coin? The answer is 'No'. And in fact, knowing the probability of each outcome can help to improve our decision-making because we can take account of the costs (or benefits) of each outcome: we simply multiply the cost by the corresponding probability and choose the outcome which leads to the lowest cost.

This is particularly valuable in domains such as medical diagnosis, where the cost of misdiagnosing someone with a serious disease is much greater than incorrectly diagnosing someone healthy: in the first case, the patient will be very ill or possibly die, whilst in the second, someone healthy might undergo a few additional tests or some unnecessary treatment.

Of course, creating a system that gives accurate estimates of probabilities is not easy: it is done by combining our initial understanding of the problem, expressed as a probabilistic prior model (this is where the view of probabilities as degrees of belief is essential), with information from experience – data, in other words. Probability theory provides a provably unique principled mechanism for doing this, which is why it is the method of choice for building models to help make decisions. Once a model has been constructed, inference is used to draw conclusions about the probability of events of interest. The field is studied by scientists under several different names: statistical pattern analysis; machine learning; and Bayesian estimation. What they have in common is the use of probability theory as a tool for understanding.

Why does this make me optimistic? There are two principal reasons: one practical and one philosophical.

The practical reason for optimism is that research, aided by modern computing power, is vastly expanding the range of problems we can tackle, whilst at the same time the number of applications that use these techniques is also growing. We are able to build more complex models more quickly: learning from data has become faster and more effective; new inference methods are being developed to cope with extremely large and interconnected systems; and we are able to calculate with more sophisticated prior models that capture ever more nuances of our understanding of different domains.

This research and the corresponding increase in the number of people who can use these techniques have led to an upsurge in the number of real applications that make use of machine learning. In medicine, for example, machine learning techniques are used to build decision-support systems, such as a stand-alone system to analyse ECGs which allows GPs to determine if a patient has a serious heart condition and thus needs priority treatment: effectively, machine learning enables us to put an expert cardiologist into a box so that their opinion can be used by a non-expert. In image analysis, the prior model encapsulates what we know about the objects we are searching for: perhaps the shape and texture of a tumour in a CT X-ray scan. We can then combine this with labelled images (ie scans in which a human expert has identified tumours) to build a system that can automatically identify tumours and grade them.

The philosophical reason for optimism comes from the worldview that is a necessary part of working in this field. At the most basic level, developing an application is necessarily a collaborative effort involving multiple disciplines: expertise in both machine learning and the problem domain is essential. Thus, sharing information and learning new ideas are an exciting and enjoyable part of my own research.

The deeper aspect of the philosophy comes from the details of how Bayes' theorem combines the prior model and observed data. With this theorem, the only events whose probability is changed with new data are those which have a non-zero probability under the prior model. An event which has zero prior probability (ie we disbelieve completely) remains at zero probability no matter how strong the evidence that it is true. In other words, we must believe that something could be true (has a non-zero probability) if we are to take account of evidence.

This implies that if we are to act rationally and be open to experience, we must allow for the possibility of different views to our own. Strict prejudging of situations impoverishes our decision-making because it does not allow for the benefits of the choices to be accounted for and closes off the possibility of increasing our understanding from new information. And that, at a time when as a society we face many very difficult decisions concerned with our health and our planet, is surely a lesson that will benefit us all. Voltaire would probably agree.

CHAPTER 8

Thinking differently

Engineering and joint replacement – developments on all fronts

David Hukins

Most of us know somebody, usually an elderly friend or relative, whose life has been transformed by an artificial hip or knee joint. However, we are not usually aware of the scientific, engineering and surgical advances that have made these devices so successful. We may also not be aware of how research is leading to continuing improvements and the application of this technology to other joints in the body.

In this short article, I will describe the kinds of research that have led to the success of hip and knee replacement, then describe progress in replacing other joints in the human body. But first, I want to describe why replacement joints are needed in the first place.

As we get older, many of us begin to suffer from osteoarthritis and rheumatoid arthritis. These diseases are associated with degeneration of joints, which become painful and stiff, making movement difficult. Although in the early stages the problems can be relieved with medication, severe degeneration can be most effectively treated by removing the joint and replacing it with an artificial one. There are other problems that can be solved by joint replacement, including congenital defects of the joint and serious injury. However, these problems tend to occur in younger people, who have higher physical expectations than the elderly, providing the impetus for improved designs.

Although artificial hips have been around for a long time, it was the pioneering work of the late Sir John Charnley in the 1960s that started to make hip replacement such a common procedure. Before then, most people with osteoarthritis or rheumatoid arthritis were condemned to living their remaining years immobile and in constant pain.

Charnley realised that most of the joints in our bodies, like our hips and knees, have remarkably low friction: about 500 times less than a comparable conventional engineering joint. His artificial hip joint had much less friction than a conventional engineering bearing because it consisted of a metal component moving within a plastic cup. The softer plastic deforms when the harder metal component pushes against it, enabling the joint to move easily without the 'seizing' that can occur in a metal-on-metal bearing. The only problem is that, over many years, movement of the metal can cause the plastic to wear. During the past 40 years, artificial joint replacement has benefitted from fundamental advances in tribology, the science of lubrication, that enable us to understand better how to reduce friction and minimise wear.

The hip is simpler than most joints in the body because it is a simple ball-and-socket joint. In hip replacement, the top of the femur (the 'thigh bone') is removed and replaced by a metal ball attached to a stem that secures it to the remaining bone. A hemi-spherical plastic cup is fitted into the pelvis so that the metal ball is free to rotate within it. In many designs, the components are held in place by 'bone cement', supplied as components that are mixed in the operating theatre and put into the patient before the mixture sets. This cement needs to be reasonably strong and have the right viscosity so that it flows into place without trapping air bubbles, so improvements and modifications continue to be developed.

Some designs of artificial joints do not need cement: they rely on bone growing up against them to hold them in place. These designs may have textured surfaces, to enable bone to secure them in place, or surface coatings which provide a better environment for bone growth than a metal surface. So developing new methods for engineering surfaces and developing new coating materials and techniques is an important part of improving artificial joints.

In recent years, an alternative approach, known as hip resurfacing, has been developed. This does not involve removing the top of the femur and so is better suited to younger patients, for whom it is advisable to remove as little bone as possible. It is also inadvisable to use a plastic cup in an artificial joint intended for younger people, because it is likely to wear out before they do! Fortunately, advances in machining and surface finishing mean that it is now possible to produce very smooth surfaces on some metals, such as cobalt-chrome alloys. Because these surfaces are very smooth, they slide over each other very easily, leading to a low friction joint that wears very slowly because all its components are metal.

The artificial knee joint is based on the same principles as the hip, although its shape and motion are much more complicated than that of a simple ball-and-socket. Knee replacement is so successful that the knee has now overtaken the hip as the most commonly replaced joint in the body. Other joints which use similar principles are the artificial shoulder, ankle and elbow.

There are also artificial replacements for the small joints in the fingers, which are based on similar principles. The main reason these joints need to be replaced is because they are damaged by rheumatoid arthritis, but because this disease often leads to deformation, it is not always feasible to fit rigid components into the bone.

An alternative is to insert artificial joints made of synthetic rubber-like materials (known as 'elastomers') into the space between the bones; the joint bends simply because the elastomer itself bends. The problem with this type of joint is that if a crack forms in the elastomer it can grow, and break the joint into two. Cracks can be initiated because the elastomer is cut by bone ends. One approach to the problem is to design joints with hard sleeves that protect the soft elastomer. However, this approach is only partially successful, so there is currently considerable research on mechanical properties and crack growth in elastomers, aimed at developing more reliable small joints.

In the past few years, a start has been made in replacing the intervertebral joints of the spine. The spine consists of a series of vertebrae linked by flexible cartilaginous structures called intervertebral discs. The natural discs are sufficiently flexible to enable the joint to twist and bend in different directions and failure of the disc can be a contributory factor in the development of back pain. However, back pain has more than one cause and is incompletely understood, so it is just as well that over 90% of cases of back pain resolve themselves without the need for any surgical intervention.

When surgery is the best option for patients with chronic back pain, the conventional operation is 'fusion' to prevent movement of the joint. Neighbouring intervertebral joints then have to compensate for the one that has been fused. Since the function of the disc is to enable the joint to twist and bend, many surgeons believe that it would be better to replace the disc than to fuse the joint. So far, most artificial discs are ball-and-socket joints, using similar principles to the artificial hip – but usually in more complicated designs. Although these artificial discs allow the joint to twist and bend they do not behave in the same way as the natural disc. The cartilaginous natural disc depends on similar principles to those used in the artificial elastomer joints for the fingers and it is possible that these same principles may be exploited to make more successful artificial intervertebral discs.

In a short article it is not possible to describe all of the science that is continuing to contribute to the success of joint replacement surgery. Topics I have left out include controlling air flow in operating theatres to reduce the risk of infection, using imaging methods to assess the performance of artificial joints in patients, using growth hormones to encourage bone growth for fixing the joints in place and many others.

We still face many challenges in making existing artificial joints even more reliable and in developing new kinds of joints. One possible approach is to use a patient's own cells to repair joints by encouraging the cells to make replacement natural tissues. This approach, called 'tissue engineering', is in its infancy but has already been used to repair cartilage.

The application of tissue engineering to replace whole joints is a long way off – and it may never happen – but it is nevertheless another area of science that needs to be explored. Challenges like this will be met by scientists, engineers and surgeons working in collaboration to solve multi-disciplinary problems.

Engineering for dancers – modelling movement

James Shippen

njury rates are higher for dancers than for footballers, Formula 1 racing drivers and builders. Not only do dancers have to jump, land, twist and stretch but they have to appear elegant and effortless at the same time. It can be no surprise therefore that placing these demands on the body often results in injuries.

Engineers know a lot about loads in structures, and what is a dancer's body if not a very complicated structure? Currently research is being undertaken to try to understand the movements of the dancer's body using engineering theory and, hopefully, in the longer term moving towards a situation where this knowledge can be used to advise the dancer on how to reduce injury rates.

The process of analysing a dancer's performance will typically commence by measuring their movements. Traditionally this has been done by taking a video of the movement, but this approach has the disadvantage of yielding only a two-dimensional image of subject, which makes accurately measuring angles and translations difficult and permanently limits the observer to the original position of the camera.

A preferable approach is to capture the dancer in three dimensions using equipment more normally found in large research hospitals or in Hollywood to create computer-animated graphics for the latest blockbuster. These techniques and equipment enable accurate measurement of the dancer's performances and have the additional advantage that it is possible to observe from any vantage point at any time in the future. However, the approach has the disadvantage that currently the equipment required for the measurement costs many thousands of pounds – though hopefully this will ease with time.

Together with the movement of the dancers, it is also important to know the external forces acting on the performers' bodies. These forces can be many times body weight and can cause injuries, especially when the body is in a posture that means it cannot resist the load. Most of this force is normally provided during contact with the floor. For example, think of the forces exerted by the floor on the dancer during landing following a large jump. However, if a pair are dancing together, the weight of the female on the male during a lift will cause large loads in his back and a horizontally cantilevered female will also experience large stresses in her back. Floor loads are typically measured by forceplates (similar to very accurate bath scales) buried into the performance floor of the laboratory.

We now have recorded the movement of the dancers and the forces that are being applied to them, which means that, together with the body mass distribution, we can calculate the torques that are occurring at all of the joints. Interesting as this is, it does not directly indicate whether an injury will result in either the short or long term. To get a step closer we must investigate how the body reacts to this situation in terms of the loads that occur in each of the muscles and at the joints. Unfortunately, it is impractical and unethical to implant load measurement devices into the muscles and joints and therefore we have to calculate these forces indirectly.

There are many more muscles in the body than the joints which they control and therefore there is not a unique solution to the distribution of loads in the muscles. To break this impasse we have to make an assumption about how the brain recruits muscles throughout the body to achieve the desired movements.

It seems reasonable to assume that the brain will attempt to turn off all the muscles as much as possible whilst still generating enough torque to overcome external forces and to move the body. This strategy can be justified by appreciating that by turning the muscles off as much as possible, the preponderance to fatigue will be reduced and this would have evolutionary benefits in the event of an unanticipated attack. Applying this assumption permits the calculation of the loads in the muscles.

A muscle which crosses a joint will not only produce a torque at the joint but will also affect the contact force which that joint experiences. As the muscles around a joint typically operate at much smaller distance than the external, inertial and gravitational forces which they counteract, the forces in the muscles can be very large and therefore so will be the joint contact forces – but it is now possible to calculate these internal joint loadings.

The mathematics for the analysis of dancers as described would have been regarded as pedestrian by Newton 300 years ago. The recent advances have been made possible by the ability to undertake the analysis within a practical time and without errors by using modern digital computing. For example, the three-dimensional reconstruction of the dancers' movements can be undertaken in real time.

The quality of the results from the analysis is very dependent on the quality of information in the biomechanical model of the dancers. The model will contain characteristics of the joint anatomy and muscle physiology. It is very difficult to obtain this information across the whole in a self-consistent manner because often the data will have to be extracted from multiple sources and synthesised into the single entity. Also, due to the complexity of human musculature and scarcity of data, it is inevitable that some muscles will not be represented in the model and it is a judgement call as to which can be safely eliminated. For example, it should not be controversial that facial muscles do not play a large locomotive role, but do the muscles associated with the hand?

Additionally, we need to improve our understanding of the injury processes that result from these loads. Dancers are not in the business of wanting to know how many Newtons of force are in their tibialis anterior or the compressive Hertzian contact load under their medial femoral epicondyle. They want to know if the steps they are performing will injure them and cut short their career, or worse.

We can compare the loads generated in the muscles with the ability of the muscles to tolerate those loads: if the former greatly exceeds the latter, injury is possible. But this is a crude criterion.

I am optimistic that engineering theory can help dancers dance better and more safely. We have made significant advances in the ability to investigate the loads experienced by dancers during rehearsal and performance, but there is still a long way to go.

Engineering and the perception of sound – it's not the sound itself

Rebecca Cain

magine the sounds of the city in Birmingham – the hum and rumble of traffic, footsteps, people sounds, it is probably quite noisy – but how do these sounds make you feel? Maybe a bit stressed, and intruded upon, or maybe they make you feel energised, like you are part of the city. Or maybe your answer would depend on why you were there in the first place, and why you were listening. Now imagine if the city were silent … how would that make you feel? Maybe slightly spooked – after all, cities are not meant to be quiet, are they?

In the past, and still to the present day, sound in urban spaces (the soundscape) has largely been thought about as noise, as something negative, which needs to be reduced. Legislation has been the biggest driver for this, with policy dictating that sound within urban spaces should not exceed certain numerical levels. However, are numerical measures always the best way to determine how sound makes someone feel? Interestingly, if we were to measure the sound pressure levels whilst standing next to a busy motorway and whilst standing on a beach watching waves crash onto the shore, we would find that in fact they are about the same – about 80–90 dB(A). But these sounds probably conjure up very different feelings within us.

There has been a growing awareness within the acoustics community that by sticking with the current paradigm of noise control, we are actually missing a trick. By starting to think of sound as a positive thing, rather than 'noise' and its negative associations, new opportunities are opening up for engineers to characterise and 'design in' positive soundscapes to our UK towns and cities. To tackle this challenge, acoustics engineers are looking beyond their own discipline for inspiration.

Desirable aspects of the soundscape have been investigated in the past, mainly by artists and social scientists, but this work has had little impact on quantitative engineering acoustics – perhaps because of barriers to communication across different disciplines. New approaches to urban sound are now emerging, an exemplar being the Positive Soundscapes Project, which is funded by the Engineering and Physical Sciences Research Council. In recognition of the need for new approaches to understanding human perception of sound and its use in planning, a team of engineers, psychologists, neurologists and other social and scientific disciplines, including sound artists, have been working together to produce a holistic approach to sound perception in the environment.

This project is a step towards a greater understanding of how scientists can analyse human perceptions of sound and how people interact with sound on a daily basis. I have been lucky to have been part of the Positive Soundscapes Project research team, bringing my engineering sound quality perspective to the mix. It has been enlightening to see and experience how methodologies and viewpoints from perspectives such as art and social science can have such a benefit on science and engineering.

The interesting thing with soundscapes is that there is usually more to their perception than the sound itself – it is usually the notion of what the sound represents that is important. For example, scientists can now engineer cars to have the perfect powerful engine 'roar' for a new sports car or a refined 'purr' for a luxury saloon – in both cases it is not really the sound itself that people are interested in, but what that sound represents.

A further complexity in understanding human perceptions of soundscapes is the changing pattern of human activities. Rich, vibrant soundscapes which encourage people to spend more time in cities may not be quite so welcoming for people for whom the city is their daily workplace, and who wish to 'tune out' intrusive sounds. Planners, architects and urban designers need a greater understanding of how humans' needs from the soundscape vary along a spectrum from being an engaged to a disengaged listener, according to their activity and purpose for being there. As we move forward, scientists and engineers can be excited about the possibilities that will open up from this new approach to urban sound, as engineers start to understand how the sound of the spaces that they design will impact upon the people who inhabit, spend time in and work in those spaces.

As engineers and scientists, we face some bold challenges with regard to our changing urban soundscapes of the future …

Perhaps one of the most exciting challenges will be understanding the change to our urban soundscapes through the shift from petrol and diesel-powered vehicles to those powered by electricity and other low-carbon technologies. These new powertrains will drastically change the soundscape of our towns and cities – but at the moment we do not know how. For this, the study of human perception of sound must move to the laboratory – to a controllable and repeatable environment where engineers can try out possibilities for future soundscapes on the people who will be affected by them, and use different methods for capturing perception – from quantitative and qualitative jury evaluations to brain scanning.

The engineering and scientific community will therefore continue to need new methods and tools not only to understand and capture human perception and behaviour in real world situations, but also to enable the increasingly sophisticated measurement of our bodies and brains in the laboratory.

Occupational health – the road to public health

Craig Jackson

t was Aristotle who declared that 'All paid jobs absorb and distort the mind' and although the level of distortion referred to may be debated, there is overwhelming evidence to show that having employment is better for one's health than the alternative. After sleep, work is the biggest sole occupier of most people's time, and the importance of its impact upon human health cannot be ignored. In fact, it should be acknowledged as a way of improving our well-being.

When pre-historic man struck one stone upon another, to fashion a blade, axe or arrowhead, he also invented the occupational hazard. In short, almost all processes that humans engage in, be they work or leisure, house the potential for short- or long-term effects upon health. In the case of our pre-historic tool-maker, the hazards were not just the sharp tool being used, or the one being made, but also the process – sparks and debris from the strike, noise and vibration from the impact, respirable dust from the clash of stones and bad posture from hunching over his work for too long.

The stone-age was the first age of occupational risk, with later smelting in the iron-age making this riskier. Despite such conditions, our non-Neanderthal friends carried on undeterred and eventually fashioned cars, microcomputers, flat panel TVs and Hadron Colliders. It can be said with confidence that pre-historic humans did not endure exposures to the modern-day hazards of psychological strain, commuting woes or line-manager bullying. Obviously there was no concept of work-related stress – there were more important things to be concerned with. Life, and the process of hunting, gathering, building and making, was much more perilous but less complex than it is now.

A seventeenth-century physician from Carpi in Northern Italy, Bernardino Ramazzini, is credited with being the first who understood the link between occupation and ill-health. His book *De Morbis Artificum Diatriba* advised doctors to follow Hippocrates' rules for diagnosis by asking patients about their symptoms, with a caveat: 'I may venture to add one more question: what occupation does he follow?' Following Ramazzini, concern was directed towards the obvious and pressing physical hazards for workers: dusts, gasses, chemicals, explosions, fire, noise and heavy loads. Occupational disease continued and evolved with the industrial revolution, resulting in the Factory Act in 1802 and an English physician, Sir Thomas Legge, later being made the first inspector of factories.

As technology and working practices developed, so too did mechanisation and jobs, and workplace dangers became more job/task-specific. The dust breathed by someone sharpening tools on a grindstone, leading to respiratory problems (silicosis), is a hazard distinctly different from the asbestos dust fibres breathed by a builder, who may develop mesothelioma. Specific safety issues evolved – loss of fingers for stonemasons; burns for those working with steam-power; and crush injuries for those working with steam engines being but a few.

Public health also suffered as a consequence of the industrial revolution, not just with workers being packed into close domestic confines, but through workplace cross contamination. Disease was passed more readily around cramped factory floors, not only through coughs, sneezes and poor hygiene practices, but also via specific working practices – such as weavers, who licked the ends of pieces of cotton on a bobbin to make them easier to thread into the shuttles that they used. As far as workers' daily health was concerned, they were dark satanic mills indeed.

Scientific investigation of potential workplace hazards and the study of hazard exposures has been the cornerstone of industrial medicine since the early 1900s. A rule of thumb that industrial hygienists and epidemiologists still use to determine if occupations are susceptible to specific diseases is to observe whether that disease is more prevalent in a given working population than in the general population, or other working populations. Hairdressers, exposed to chemicals and water through persistent hair washing, tend to have more skin diseases such as eczema and contact dermatitis (cases) than office workers or the general population who do not endure such exposures (controls).

This case-control approach to occupational disease spotting has been able to inform us of many important trends and developments in worker ill-health in hundreds of industries. Examples include musculoskeletal disorders among miners (poor postures and heavy work); asthma problems in bakers (flour dust); clusters of childhood leukaemia in the children of power plant workers (non-ionising radiation); and hearing problems in metal plate workers (loud factory processes).

Two turning points with massive impact upon work and disease occurred in the mid-1990s. The first was a shift away from occupational medicine's focus on the traditional physical causes of disease: chemicals, ergonomics, gasses, fumes, long working hours, shift work, metals, toxins, viruses and dusts. Instead, occupational science changed focus towards psychological hazards as a root cause of many health problems in the workplace, rather than physical ones. This biopsychosocial perspective followed the philosophical unification view that the mind and body were unified, and any troubles that bothered the psyche would also trouble the soma: the mind and body were unified and reflected the health, or ill-health, of each other.

This change of focus occurred after occupational medicine was unable scientifically to explain some unusual large-scale cases of workplace ill-health via the biomedical model. Mysterious health problems in the 1990s (repetitive strain injury, sick building syndrome, a whole gamut of musculoskeletal soft-tissue injuries in the absence of physical trauma and the infamous Gulf war syndrome) all failed to be associated with reliable and consistent physical hazards. Gulf war syndrome affected several thousand veterans of the first Gulf war, with symptoms ranging from fatigue, depression, anxiety, flu-like symptoms and sensitivities to some chemicals – all present in different combinations and intensities in sufferers. This lack of consistency in symptoms and hazard exposure for sufferers led to a failing in attributing Gulf war syndrome to any physical causes, and it was therefore viewed as having psychological (pre-disposing) causes rather than physical ones. This turning point marked the existential age of 'if you believe you're ill, then you're ill' in the workplace, and the psychosocial self-diagnostic door to workplace ill-health was opened.

A second turning point was a management volt-face concerning workers and their personal problems. The 1990s saw, for probably the first time in modern line-management standards, the acceptance that workers' personal problems were to be acknowledged as impacting upon their workplace well-being. As the UK entered the post-Diana age of emotional outpouring, the adage that workers should leave their personal problems at the door was outdated, and workplaces had to take account of personal circumstances as possible contributory factors to any ill-health. Personality type, attitudes and past experience can all combine together to produce a catastrophic individual.

A distressed person, doing depressing or stressful work, would therefore be a very depressed worker indeed, and this view of the worker as a psychological entity is still currently dominant. Such distress, if untreated, would eventually lead to ill-health via two mechanisms: first, there would be a genuine physical manifestation of symptoms as an extension of psychological distress and, secondly, when distressed or unhappy, tolerance to physical symptoms reduces, making complaints or help-seeking more likely.

To some, the notion that persistent lower back ache could develop through psychological distress alone seems like an anathema, and it is less than two centuries since medical knowledge thought that unhappiness was a cause of pellagra, beri beri, or even Down's syndrome. Only the future will show if contemporary thinking is correct. Either way, the self-diagnostic door to workplace ill-health was flung as wide open as it would go.

So why my optimism, if workplaces are full of workers who may only be one-bad-day-too-many away from going off sick with musculoskeletal disorders, or repetitive strain injuries, or the perennial of workplace stress? Absences due to work-related stress have increased in the UK by approximately 250,000 new cases each year since 2001. The explanation may not be a straightforward one, but it could be related to UK working patterns: the UK has more full-time workers as a percentage of the workforce than any other EU country; the UK works more full-time hours than any other EU country; and UK workers put in more unpaid overtime than any other EU country. Despite the overworked and sickly outlook of workplaces at present, regression to the mean can only suggest that improvements in workplaces will be sure to come. The lot of a typical working person in the UK will be improved by legislation, humanism and good practice.

Pre-employment health screening will be more common – helping to ensure that potential staff are fit for their job and allowing the identification of staff with health problems who may need support in order to carry out their roles successfully. This could cover a range of risk factors, from those with genetic susceptibility to skin cancer who apply for outdoor jobs; younger workers with acquired hearing loss (iPod syndrome) working in warehouses with constant streams of forklift trucks; to those who may be susceptible to certain allergies if working with animals or chemicals. Coupled with this, routine health surveillance should be used in the workplace to keep a check on the health of workers, especially those who have pre-disposing factors.

People are essentially 'voluntarily trapped' in their workplaces for between eight and 12 hours a day on average – far longer than they would spend in a gym or taking exercise. With thoughtful architectural design and careful planning, workplaces can be engineered to increase 'ambient exercise' and keep people active – the concept of occupational rehabilitation is not new. Setting escalators to slow speeds (to encourage taking the stairs); locating departments as far away from each other as possible;

Epidemiology – making the right connections

Graham Medley

Optimism implies three things: future, probability and judgement. I cannot be optimistic about the past since it has already happened. I can only be optimistic when I have the option of being pessimistic – I cannot be optimistic about things that I know will turn out well. Human perception determines what 'turn out well' means; the universe is not optimistic, it just does. Tigers will go extinct in the wild (no room for optimism there), but ecology, and human society, will keep going. It is also easier, I think, to be optimistic about things that I know nothing about, so I will stick to my subject.

I work in infectious disease epidemiology, and my approach is essentially ecological, treating the pathogen-host interaction as an ecologist treats a predator-prey interaction. I collect data to understand the dynamic interactions between (at least) two populations, use statistical models to develop and test hypotheses about the relationships and devise mathematical models to explore the potential dynamics and, ultimately, to predict the impact of interventions such as immunisation and quarantine. I can make this approach sound like the solution to all infectious disease problems, and have done so pretty successfully in the past. During my career, infectious disease epidemiology has changed from an interesting scientific inquiry to almost engineering-like rigour of design and assessment of interventions.

How will the subject develop? I am sure that infectious disease will continue to plague humankind and the animals and plants that they care about for the rest of my career – as well as the careers of all my past, current and future students. It will be good for our careers, but does imply that disease will continue to exact its tolls. I know that the quality of data will increase, and that new methods will be developed to analyse the data: the biological understanding will get deeper. Old paradoxes and conundrums will be resolved, and new ones will appear. We can do things now that were impossible dreams when I started my research career (in 1983), and I expect that my students will have the same experience. Our mechanistic understanding of how things work will improve, and some of these explanations will coalesce: old knowledge will be destroyed by new theories.

I am pessimistic that reductionist science will continue to dominate infectious disease epidemiology. But optimistic that the interdisciplinarity that is emerging will have far-reaching consequences, and that our understanding will widen as well as deepen. Jan Smuts' vision of a holistic science is probably no closer now than it was a century ago, but there is a realisation that if scientific understanding is to change human actions for the better, then the science has to address the problems rather than just addressing the problems it can solve. And it is deciding what the problem is, so-called 'problem framing', that I am most excited about.

The twentieth century showed how bad things could be when human systems (economic, political etc) go wrong. We should, and probably are, working with moderate success to ensure that some of the same things do not happen again. I hope (but not very confidently) that we do not have to learn similar lessons about ecology in the twenty-first century – that it can be really bad if we do not pay attention to the system-level interactions among people and between people and the environment. Increasingly, we have come to realise that social-ecological systems are what we should be studying to find out what problems require a solution – and how that solution can be implemented.

As I write, the UK is in the middle of the first wave of the H1N1 influenza epidemic that was first detected in Mexico. It has been named 'swine flu' by the media, though it has little to do with pigs. But as a result of this name, Egypt decided to intervene by slaughtering its pig population, and many countries banned the import of pig products. Had the media latched on to the name 'Mexican flu', then no doubt Mexico and Mexicans would have been blamed for a purely ecological process.

After a period of panic, the UK population seems to have settled for a more pragmatic view. It has even been said that it is better to get infected with H1N1 influenza now, rather than later, in case it mutates to become more pathogenic. There has also been talk of 'influenza parties', at which people can deliberately become infected. The disease has changed social interactions, and social interactions have changed the disease.

I am currently working on governance of livestock disease in a multidisciplinary grant funded by the Rural Economy and Land Use (RELU) programme. The programme was set up largely as a consequence of the foot and mouth disease (FMD) epidemic that resulted in over 6.5 million livestock being culled and cost billions of pounds. We are studying the interaction between epidemiology, politics, economics and law in determining the patterns of livestock disease, and how the disease, in turn, affects these dimensions and their interactions.

The programme is itself an indication of this process, since the resources spent have been as a consequence of an epidemic, and will have an effect on future epidemics, but not necessarily just FMD. A key idea of our project is that we are treating several diseases simultaneously, since interventions (and changes in human activity generally) will have an impact on all diseases, not just the target. For example, the 'influenza parties' will also result in increased transmission of everything else, just as stopping movement of cattle between farms during FMD will have had an impact on every other cattle disease.

Humans organise themselves into collective action that shapes infectious disease patterns, and infectious disease in turn then shapes society. Understanding these processes better will enable us to define the problems more acutely, and we will be able to develop natural and social scientific approaches to address these real problems. This is what I am optimistic about – even if it does not produce any results, it is going to be very interesting.

Inorganic elements – a new way of tackling disease

Peter Sadler

I am optimistic about the prospects for discovery. Discovery is exciting. There is a lot of it still to be done.

My field is inorganic chemistry, the chemistry of the periodic table, those 100-plus elements that determine everything we do: what our universe is made of, how the body's biochemistry works, the drugs we can make, the clothes we can wear, the TV screens we can watch and so on – the fabric, the substance, of life.

I work on the interdisciplinary borders of inorganic chemistry, biology and medicine. Which of the 81 stable elements on earth are essential for life? Probably about 25 of them, but several of these and others have question marks against them – we are not really sure if we need them or not, and in other cases we think we need them but do not understand what they do in the body. Plenty of challenges, scope for discovery.

Surely genomes can tell us. Genomes are the blueprints of life. They code for everything. Or do they? Genomes (DNA) code for proteins. Proteins (enzymes) can synthesise other molecules. Together they should determine which elements we need for life.

Yes, this is certainly true for many common essential elements. We can recognise the DNA codes for proteins that bind to iron. The uptake, transport and distribution and excretion of iron in the body is carefully controlled by proteins. When we take in too much the uptake pathway is switched off; when we have too little it is switched on (homeostasis). At least one organism is known that does not need iron (the Lyme disease pathogen, Borrelia burgdorferi), and sure enough the codes for iron proteins are absent from its genome. We can read the genomes for codes for other metals such as copper and zinc and even the non-metal selenium, which is inserted into proteins as a substitute for sulphur by a complicated series of events.

But what about vanadium, chromium, nickel or tin, for example? These are thought to be essential metals for us but we know very little about their biochemistry or their genetic codes. If they are essential then we should be using them in medicine, controlling their uptake, recognising deficiency and excess symptoms, designing new drugs for treatment of related conditions.

This in itself offers new challenges. Many inorganic elements are more difficult to study than carbon, the basis of so many of our therapies (organic compounds). Bonds to metals are usually weaker than to carbon and can make and break on a very wide range of timescales (nanoseconds to years). We need new techniques for such studies – challenges, scope for discovery.

Even elements with household names like fluorine (fluoridated water, toothpastes) are in need of more attention. We think that fluoride strengthens minerals in our teeth (fluoroapapite), but what else can it do in the body? How is it transported and stored?

Its congener, chloride, is known to have specific (DNA-coded) transport pathways into cells, which, when they go wrong, are the basis of disease (cystic fibrosis). We know that iodine is incorporated into hormones (thyroid hormones), and that leaves bromine as the remaining stable element of group 17 (the halogens) to consider. There are micromolar levels of bromine in our blood and it may play a role in helping to kill invading organisms (eg bacteria) but we know too little to label bromine as essential. More need for investigation and discovery.

Radioactive elements have their place in medicine as diagnostic agents, but presumably not as essential elements. Indeed natural radon is said to be the second biggest cause of lung cancer behind smoking. But what about potassium-40, a radioactive isotope of an element we certainly need in our cells? Every second about 2,500 atoms of potassium-40 decay in our bodies and there seems little that we can do to prevent this. No doubt the damage is slight and in any case we have enzymes that can repair our DNA.

The key to advances in the understanding and use of the elements of the periodic table in medicine is speciation. It is not just the element that matters, but its charge (oxidation state) and the other atoms that bind strongly to it. It is not sufficient to say we need the element; we may need specific compounds of that element. Vitamin B12, a cobalt compound, is a good example. Then there is arsenic. Arsenobetaine, made, for example, by sea creatures such as lobsters and flat fish, is a specific arsenic compound, relatively non-toxic. Arsenic trioxide is now approved as a front-line treatment for certain types of leukaemia. We can expect to see advances in the design of new arsenic drugs, but this is currently hampered by the difficulties involved in studying arsenic chemistry – another challenge for discovery.

Perhaps it is the inorganic elements that hold the key to understanding some currently intractable diseases, especially those relating to the brain – Parkinson's, Alzheimer's, senile dementia etc. For example, there is iron, manganese, copper and zinc in the brain, often localised in specific areas, mobilised during specific events. We need to understand how to control these.

It is true that lithium is widely used for the treatment of bipolar disorders (eg manic depression), that gold drugs have been used for the treatment of rheumatoid arthritis for over 70 years, that tonnes of gadolinium have been injected into patients over the last few years as contrast agents for MRI scans and that platinum-based drugs account for about 6% of the global anticancer drug market. The stimulus for establishing inorganic chemistry as a necessary part of biology and medicine is not hard to illustrate.

So much still to discover – and I am optimistic that the exploration will be exciting and worthwhile.

Microbiology –
the key to life on earth

Peter Lambert

In July 1969 I was one of millions of people around the world who watched a series of grainy black and white television pictures recording the Apollo 11 mission to the moon. The fear and insecurity of the Sputnik satellite, circling 500 miles above our earth at 18,000 miles an hour just 12 years earlier, was the driving force for one of the greatest human achievements. The most beautiful image, perhaps the most reproduced image of all time, was the colour view of the earth taken from the moon. In stark contrast to the arid desolation of the moon, our earth appeared as a beautiful pearly blue and white sphere. For me this was the realisation that we live in a very precious and vulnerable place. If the earth were an apple, we live and breathe in the tiny, vulnerable region represented by the skin.

In the 40 years since Apollo 11 we have all come to understand that we must look after our environment. We all now recognise that the big issues facing us are how to secure power and food supplies that do not upset the balance of the earth. Microbiologists study the smallest living cells, so what can we do to help? The tiny cells we study, a millionth of a meter long, could hold the key to many of the problems we now face in maintaining our environment. This is what I am optimistic about.

Microbiology is the key to life on earth. Our planet is 4.5 thousand million years old and microbes have been here for over three-quarters of that time. The microbes put oxygen into the atmosphere and provided the environment for the more complex life to evolve. In the lifetime of the earth, humans have been here for a very short time, the last hundred thousand years for *Homo sapiens*. If the lifetime of the earth were compressed into 24 hours, we have only been here for the last two seconds before midnight.

Microbes are still here. Given their track record of survival, it should come as no surprise that they occupy every possible part of our world. The oceans, rivers and soil contain an amazing variety of different microbes. We are only now realising how diverse they are and the vital part they play in regulating the environment. Huge numbers of microbes are very close to all of us. They are on our skin and in the contents of our intestines. There are ten microbes in our bodies for every single cell – we are outnumbered by ten to one. Generally they do us no harm, in fact they help us digest our food and supply us with many vital vitamins. It is only when this balance is upset that we have problems with infections. Even then it is the antibiotics, the products of other microbes, that come to our rescue.

By understanding what makes microbes work, we have learned how to manipulate them. Genetic engineering and biotechnology have given us the tools to change microbes so that they produce safer and more effective medicines. We can use the same techniques in agriculture to improve crop yields and make crops drought resistant. Technologies developed from microbes help us treat disease and feed us – can they do more?

The biggest problem we face is to find sources of energy that do not contaminate our world. We are on track to do this through harnessing the sun, wind and waves as renewable, non-polluting sources of energy. It might just be the case that microbes will help in this quest. Microbes naturally present in the sea and rivers are continually removing toxic and contaminating material. Our public health system uses microbes to purify our waste water, restoring it to a quality suitable for drinking. In doing so, the microbes generate energy. Could we think of a way to couple the decontaminating properties of these obliging microbes to the energy they produce?

Microbial fuel cells could provide the answer. First investigated nearly 100 years ago, these devices use microbes in a chamber to consume the contaminating chemicals in waste water and pass on the energy in the form of electricity to an electrode. Tiny fuel cells of this kind are available for schools to demonstrate the principle, using baker's yeast and sugar. Rapid improvements are being made in the efficiency and power that they produce. To date they generate only tiny amounts of power, about 1 watt for each square metre of electrode in the cells. This is enough to light a very small bulb, power a calculator or wristwatch or turn a small fan.

Can this be scaled up further to generate real power from domestic and industrial waste water? We had the optimism and belief in technology in the 1960s to send people to the moon, so why not?

Orangutan locomotion – illustrating our place in nature

Susannah Thorpe

'Man is rated the highest animal, at least among all animals who returned the questionnaire.'

Robert Brault (2009)

The year 2009 was the one hundred and fiftieth anniversary of Charles Darwin's publication of *On the Origin of Species*. In this seminal work Darwin introduced his theory of evolution by natural selection, a theory that has become the foundation of all biological study. Surprisingly though, it was another British biologist, Thomas Henry Huxley, who first addressed the relationship between humans and other animals in his 1863 thesis, 'Evidence as to Man's Place in Nature'. In this rather prescient work he noted the anatomical similarities between humans, gibbons, orangutans, gorillas and chimpanzees; relationships formalised by Linnaeus' classifications into lesser apes (gibbons) and great apes (orangutans, chimpanzees, gorillas and humans), and confirmed by recent genetic analysis.

But not all of Victorian society welcomed Huxley's idea that humans might, like chimpanzees and gorillas, be simply another African ape. Upon hearing the news, the wife of the Bishop of Worcester is quoted as saying: 'Descended from the apes! My dear, let us hope that this is not true, but if it is, let us pray that it will not become generally known!' Of course, 150 years later, it is well known, but that does not mean that it is well accepted.

Throughout recent history, humans have sought, both consciously and subconsciously, to identify how we differ from the rest of the animal kingdom; how our intelligence, culture, emotions, anatomy and behaviour set us apart from our animal cousins. But the last decade has seen considerable advances in our understanding of the relationship between humans and other animals. The optimism that I would like to share is that research is finally breaking down these self-created barriers, embedding humankind and our evolution soundly into the animal kingdom.

The ancestors of modern humans and modern chimpanzees separated about six million years ago. The split is widely thought to be associated with the evolution of bipedal walking in human ancestors (hominins), but much debate has surrounded how bipedalism evolved. The traditional hypothesis argues that because chimpanzees and gorillas knuckle-walk (on all fours but with their fingers partially flexed) on the ground, the origins of bipedalism must be understood in this context. Others have noted that that when climbing up vertical tree trunks, the great apes extend their legs in a manner that would 'pre-adapt' the body for bipedalism; that is to say, that the adaptation of bipedalism would be a relatively easy affair for an animal that was good at vertical climbing. Still others have proposed that human ancestors, smaller and weaker than the other apes, were forced out of the receding forests during the Miocene, and landed, rather fortuitously, on the banks of marine habitats where the was an abundance of accessible aquatic food resources, and where habitual bipedalism evolved in response to the selective benefits accrued by wading through shallow water whilst foraging. The latter, though compelling, lacks any fossil evidence in its support, and the evidence for the former two is highly contested.

My own research has contributed to this debate. Through studying the locomotion of wild orangutans in Indonesia, my colleagues and I found that orangutans use arboreal bipedalism in the trees to access the most flexible branches at the periphery of tree crowns, where the majority of tasty fruits and the narrowest gaps between tree crowns (necessary for safe arboreal travel) are situated. Indeed, all the great apes use bipedalism in some form, suggesting that, far from being a defining feature of humanity, bipedalism is a general ape adaptation that has simply become more specialised in humans.

Our research is not alone in blurring the human–other ape divide. Theories that humans are unique in exhibiting culture, for example, are also looking increasingly outdated. Certainly art, theatre, literature and music indicate a level of cultural sophistication not present elsewhere in the animal kingdom, but cultural evolution at its core is socially learned behaviours that are passed down the generations and enhance the fitness of the animal. Orangutans at Suaq Balimbing in North Sumatra, unlike all other populations, blow 'raspberries' in the final phase of nest building – a social signal that seems to announce that the sender is bedding down for the night. Chimpanzees in West Africa use stones and pieces of wood to crack open nuts for food; but this has never been observed in chimps living in East Africa.

Since all the living great apes exhibit culture, far from being a human phenomenon, it is highly likely that the common ancestor of great apes did too, taking the origins of culture to at least 16 million year ago. But culture is not even unique to apes – male humpback whales sing long, complex songs in tropical waters during the breeding season. All of the whales in a population sing the same song at any one time, but this differs significantly from the songs of other populations; a cultural adaptation that seems to increase the breeding success of some whale populations.

Numerous other so-called human traits have been observed in the other apes. Orangutans, chimpanzees and gorillas all squeal in response to tickling, and new research suggests this behaviour may be the evolutionary root of laughter. Conversely, the territorial behaviour of chimpanzees, in which groups have been observed to hunt and kill members of neighbouring troops systematically, is an eerie parallel of human warfare, and differences in how this behaviour is expressed in two such closely related species may offer clues to war's evolutionary origins. Chimpanzees also have their own version of the sex trade: wild male chimps that share meat with females double their chances of having sex with those females, and thus passing on their genes to the next generation.

These similarities are not anthropomorphic illusions, but conclusions drawn from objective scientific research. They tell us that humans are not unique and that many differences between humans and the other apes are in fact a matter of degrees rather than a fundamental disparity. But does that imply that other apes are merely primitive, less 'evolved' forms of humans? If both humans and chimpanzees practise warfare, why did humans and not chimps develop the atomic bomb? If both humans and orangutans use bipedalism, why did orangutans not come down out of the trees and stride out bipedally onto the savannah to dominate the world?

The answer of course is that differences between species must be viewed in relation to their habitat. Chimpanzee warfare is highly effective in rainforest habitats and in relation to the frequency with which chimpanzees troops meet neighbouring groups. Similarly, it was human rather than orangutan ancestors that descended to the ground and developed terrestrial bipedalism because when the forests started fragmenting over six million years ago and tremendous competition arose for diminishing forest fruits, human ancestors lost the competition and were forced to look for food in other habitats. Thus recent research has helped to reveal that other apes and indeed all other animals are not by any means inferior to humans, but are uniquely adapted to the habitat in which they move, feed and reproduce.

So, why is it important that humans are viewed as part of the animal kingdom? It allows us to pose more questions about animal (including human) evolution and better to define what those questions should be. It has the potential to help us understand the evolutionary origins of human behaviour, and perhaps even help us change those behaviours; the lessons that we learn through observing chimpanzee warfare may perhaps help us break our own violent habits.

Accepting that humans are part of the animal kingdom helps us to unravel the special adaptations that we have to our habitat, just as it helps us to understand the special adaptations of orangutans or chimps. I am also optimistic that it will help us to understand how we should treat other creatures, whilst respecting their unique emotions, intelligence and ability to feel pain.

But we have a hurdle that we must jump before we can achieve these goals. Whilst humans have expanded to virtually every habitable part of the planet, chimpanzees, gorillas and orangutans are fighting for survival, largely because of habitat destruction caused by us. Indeed, if Indonesian rainforests continue to be destroyed at current rates, then it has been predicted that the Sumatran orangutan, the subject of my research, will be extinct in the wild within a decade. That prediction was made three years ago, and deforestation has not slowed down.

Just when we are beginning to understand human's place in nature, we are driving to extinction the species that form our animal family. This global problem must be arrested if we are to maintain the grandeur of the animal kingdom for the future generations of all species and for future species.

Biological inheritance – following complex pathways

Jack Cohen

'There is so much quantitative data in biology now, particularly the various "-omics" in cell and molecular biology, that it has overwhelmed the hypothesis-driven science that starts with a question ...'

Anon (2009)

So let us start with a question: 'How many progeny breed?' This seems to be so broad a question that no answer is possible. But that is not so. In normal circumstances, with the same number of organisms in successive generations, the answer is obvious: two parents in this generation make two parents in the next! This is a very interesting answer, because although it must be true in general, it is not so for any particular pair of parents. A female starling lays about 16 eggs in her life, and on average around two will breed and 14 will die without breeding, mostly having been eaten when young.

Darwin, and separately Wallace, picked up from Malthus the general issue that offspring always greatly outnumber the parents of the next generation. Natural selection reduces the surplus, the less well-adapted, down to approximately the right number – hence evolution. But neither saw the simplicity, that two parents in this generation make two parents in the next. That is as true of codfish, which produce 80 million or more eggs in a lifetime, as it is of frogs, producing ten thousand, or elephants, producing five. An oak tree, producing tens of thousands of acorns each year, on average just replaces itself. This is the central issue for conservation, of course. (David Attenborough's TV series *The Trials of Life* aimed to celebrate it, having been provoked by my book, *Reproduction*.)

There are two interesting questions here, neither of which we can begin to answer! The genetic question: which offspring survive to breed? (Their breeding must generate the same diversity in the next generation.) And the ecological question: what is the nature of the 'bottleneck' that finally places the future parents – and only the future parents – in their niches?

We misunderstood the genetics of wild populations in the twentieth century. We started wrongly, with agricultural populations, or fruit flies or mice inbred in laboratory culture. The great triumph of neo-Darwinism was to combine Mendel's results, explained by chromosomes and later by DNA, with inbred populations, and to come out with – uncommon – mutations to explain diversity. This is the 'folk knowledge' of biological inheritance, and it is wrong.

Only in the early 1970s did it become possible to investigate the genetics of real, wild organisms, without breeding them: Lewontin's group showed, by determining whether one or two versions of each of many proteins were prescribed, that there was immensely more variation than neo-Darwinism had imagined. Instead of mutations being rare, 10% of genes in an organism were represented by two versions, different versions – alleles – from Ma and Pa. At least 30% of genes had two or more versions, scattered in the population!

That is to say, many ancient mutations were – are – still with us: it was not the case that all mutations were tested promptly to see if they were 'good' (made the carrier genetically 'fitter', producing more progeny) and therefore adopted, or 'bad' (reducing progeny), hence disappearing.

So, rather than looking at a litter of mice to see which had the 'good' gene mutation or which the 'bad', we now had to assume that all the offspring had some good, some bad – furthermore, good only in some circumstances, depending on what other alleles of other genes were present,

Under the flag of neo-Darwinism, there had been a belief that nearly all these alleles were 'neutral' in their effects, but this was shown experimentally not to be so. So how can natural selection discriminate at all consistently, when each of the progeny naturally has a unique recombination of mother's and father's gene alleles? They cannot 'breed true' into the next generation.

This puts us right back to Darwin's position: he could see variation among offspring, but could not consign it to a consistent genetic mechanism. We could see, in the twentieth century, how the 'folk story', the simple mutational theory of neo-Darwinism, could result in more or fewer copies in the next generation: we could follow the complications that could render mutations dominant, for example. But we now know that real, wild genomes are not like that. We cannot now see how the complexity of real wild genomes can lead to a simple – or even a complicated – mechanism of phenotypic inheritance: offspring resembling parents!

I am confident that the clue is there: complexity. Not simple or even complicated, but complex. Surely, there are clues in all those numbers, all those '-omics'. It has turned out that cell biology is immensely complex – where we anticipated simplicity at the level of The Cell as the Unit of Life, there is immense complexity. There are hundreds of thousands of proteins, some of them being chaperones and making sure others fold up correctly (even if they are somewhat mutant), some of them being designed to tag on to short, specific lengths of DNA and modify gene activity, some of them being cell-surface receptors for, for example, insulin – and hundreds being quite like insulin-receptors but importantly different! But the real complexity is just being discovered now. And it is this: many functions for RNA.

It was so nice and clear and simple when we had the DNA with gene sequences along it, and the RNA messenger carrying the sequence out of the nucleus, where the ribosomes would assemble proteins according to the sequence, transfer RNA's lifting amino-acids into position ... There was all that space between genes, that some of us called 'junk' DNA (because we could not easily imagine a more complex story). What a nice simple story that was! It now turns out that RNA, made as long sequences, or as 21- or 28-nucleotide lengths, mostly from those 'spaces' between the genes in the DNA, is the major control of which genes are turned on, by how much etc. And it is recursive: some are destroyed but many are used again and again – in different places, different functions. There is complexity, with knobs on!

There are three groups of biologists who might unravel this story, and achieve explanations – again – of why offspring resemble parents. The first are the number-crunchers, the genomics, proteomics, all the other '-omics' collectors and describers. I do not expect to get usable explanations from that lot, just descriptions of what is happening, not why.

The second group, the biosemioticians, interpret much of the complexity as coding: not only the DNA and RNA codes, but the insulin molecule getting interpreted by its receptor, so that different things happen inside a cell when it sticks to the outside. Interpreting so much of cellular biochemistry as codes, all the receptors and messenger molecules in cells, even the complex RNA effects as codes, allows explanation ... but we must wait to see whether the RNA recursional effects can be turned into useful explanation.

I am optimistic that there is a third group of biologists, hand-in-glove with the semioticians and ready to use the data from the '-omics' group, who will work with the emergent properties of the system rather than the biochemistry. Just as a bridge can be made of rope, concrete or steel, and still show its important – emergent – properties, so I am sure that higher-level biological properties – those ways in which offspring resemble parents, for example – are not achieved through meticulous follow-through of the detail, but through emergent properties.

And we will not get explanation through detailed biochemistry, but through codes, or through 'Ant Country': very complex pathways, different in detail, that result in the same end product. Then at last we will understand how genetic diversity can be maintained through the generations, and how individual organisms get selected as breeders. But I am afraid that we are not close to that yet. '

We will, in the next 20 years, get a whole new explanation of how and why offspring resemble their parents, why Francis Darwin, the old man's great-grandchild, was the spitting image of the young Charles Darwin, despite having but one-sixteenth of the same genes – same snub nose, same ears. And we might come to understand how all four grandparents, cooing over the new baby, all see their own family characteristics: 'Look at that, he's got Ernie's ears … and see how he's got that smile – it's just like you had when you were that age! That nose, unmistakeable, it's Uncle Fred to a "T" …'

When we can explain that, we will begin to understand heredity.

Positivity – staying connected

Michael West

Over the last ten years there has been a transformation in the study of human behaviour from a focus predominantly on neuroses, pathology and dysfunction to a new fascination with strengths, potential and values in human behaviour. This new orientation has revealed astonishing and immensely encouraging ways to promote health and well-being among people, groups and communities. It offers powerful and practical implications for how to help people live their lives more fully and how to create work organisations which are effective and which provide employees with environments within which they can thrive.

We have discovered that positive emotion is associated with a range of benefits, including longevity (positive people live ten years longer), income, marital satisfaction, sleep quality, susceptibility to colds, strokes and diabetes and recovery from trauma. The research evidence convincingly shows that it is positivity which leads to success rather than success to positivity. Positivity encompasses all those feelings we describe by the words gratitude, serenity, interest, hope, pride, amusement, inspiration, awe and of course love. These effects are demonstrable at the cellular level as well as at the social level. Positivity is associated with cell growth rather than decay, more bonding hormones (associated with relationship building) and fewer stress hormones.

One reason for this is that positive emotion encourages us to broaden our experiences, thereby building our capacities in life. When we feel positive we are more likely to take the risk of trying new experiences such as a new food, a sporting activity, speaking with a stranger in a lift or going to a new and different theatre production. These experiences then become assimilated into our experience as a part of our behavioural repertoire on which we can build. We can build on these now familiar experiences to extend our experience thereby further building our behaviours, skills and knowledge. Positivity leads people to broaden and build in their lives.

This would not make me optimistic if the research also suggested that positivity was largely genetically determined. There is certainly evidence for a considerable heritable component to positive affectivity, but there is much to show that people can learn how to think more positively, feel more gratitude and expect positive outcomes in their lives. Not only can these orientations be learned, but leaders in organisations can make a difference by creating positive, supportive and appreciative cultures at work which foster positive feelings among employees. They in turn are happier at work, more creative and much more likely to co-operate with and support their colleagues, and more likely to encourage satisfaction among customers.

The research does not suggest that being constantly and irritatingly chipper or 'happy clappy' all the time is the route to everlasting peace and happiness. Faking positive emotion repeatedly may be more stressful than being curmudgeonly. The research suggests that positive emotion needs to be balanced by negative experiences but the balance has to be predominantly in the direction of positive experience. Some mathematical modelling suggests that a ratio of around 3:1 of positive to negative experiences is about right for most people. Negative emotions are an important part of life – sadness, fear and anger serve important purposes for us. But having predominantly positive experiences of gratitude, serenity, interest, hope, pride, amusement, inspiration, awe and love is what makes for human health. In marriages, those with positive to negative interaction ratios of around 5:1 are the most successful.

But the negative emotions are components of relationships too. Anger and engagement are important (within limits) in relationships to enable couples to work through problems towards new understanding; expressions and experiences of disgust and contempt, however, indicate a poor prognosis for marriage survival. And in general, there seems a limit to positivity. The mathematical modelling suggests an upper bound of positive to negative experiences of around 11:1.

These benefits of positivity extend to the world of work also. For example, physicians who are induced to feel mildly positive make better diagnoses, more fully considering all the options. My research in more than 50 manufacturing organisations has shown that the number of positive statements made by CEOs predicts employee attitudes a year later, which in turn predicts company productivity. Studies of top management teams have examined whether their interactions in meetings are positive or negative, self- or other-focused, and whether they are focused on inquiry or advocacy of a position. The most successful teams have a ratio of 6:1 of positive, other-focused and inquiry interactions rather than negative, self-focused and advocacy interactions. And company performance in such teams is much better as a consequence. Positive people make the best negotiators – their co-operative and friendly orientations produce the best deals for themselves and their negotiating partners. People trust positive people more than others. These benefits and others have also been demonstrated in schools, where positivity programmes have been introduced.

What makes me optimistic too is the evidence that positivity induces a feeling of connectedness between people – there is less separation between the concepts of 'me' and 'you'. We recognise faces of those from our own race much more effectively than we do the faces of people from races other than our own. This is an important indicator of racial separation, but inducing positive emotions in people during experiments has the effect of dramatically reducing or eliminating these racially cued differences in face recognition. It seems positivity leads to unconscious reductions in racial stereotyping.

Positive attitudes among team members towards cultural and racial diversity is the best predictor of how diverse teams perform, and diverse teams which get on well clearly outperform homogenous teams in both levels of productivity and innovation. We desperately need people from different backgrounds to learn how to work together effectively in our world. Having positive attitudes towards the value of difference enables such effective working, and it is easy to learn. The first step is knowing where you are now, and you can use a psychometric measure to tell you (see www.positivityratio.com) very quickly.

And if you want to increase positivity, how is this to be achieved? Certainly not by faking it. The prescriptions from this research are:

- To practise being open to others and to life.
- To create high quality connections with others by being present, attentive and affirming in all interactions.
- To cultivate kindness – being kind to others induces very positive emotions in us and in relationships.
- Develop distractions to help you avoid ruminating continually on negative experiences or thoughts. Physical activities or gardening seem particularly potent distractions but so do many other activities that stretch you, such as dancing, walking, cooking, sports, learning new skills, helping out your friends and engaging with others in voluntary activities.
- Dispute negative thinking by challenging it – dispute thoughts that you will do badly, not be successful, never get what you want, disappoint those you love.
- Find nearby nature because time spent in natural surroundings induces positive emotions.
- And 30 years after I completed my PhD on the Psychology of Meditation, many psychologists are now presenting evidence showing that meditation is a powerful way of developing health, well-being and positivity.
- Ritualise gratitude by writing down once a week what you have had to be grateful for that week and feel the benefits.

- Above all, savour and build your loving relationships: with partner, family and friends.

Many people in the world face situations which are appalling and, of course, positivity in those circumstances may perhaps seem a vacuous concept, but even in the inhuman and hopeless environment of Nazi concentration camps, Frankl reports on the redeeming value of kindness and love.

None of this is new to us intuitively but what is encouraging is the extensive and persuasive evidence base that supports what philosophers and religions have advocated for centuries. As head of a business school, this research provides me with a clear mission to create organisations characterised by positive climates, where people feel engaged, excited and energised by their work; where leaders provide principled, just and inspiring leadership; where people feel appreciated, respected and supported; and where there is a strong sense of values and integrity. Organisations must also be positive places, focused on making a contribution to society and community to ensure they are institutions with a sense of connectedness.

CHAPTER 9

From where I stand

Biomaterials science – a scientist's story

Brian Tighe

My optimism for the future of biomaterials science and its contribution to the problem of human ageing is reinforced by the story of the Czechoslovakian chemist Otto Wichterle – for two principal reasons. The first is the example of his determination to succeed in the face of scientific and political opposition; the second is the fact that his innovative thinking not only formed the basis of the multi-billion dollar soft contact lens industry but also encapsulated a principle that underpins the current wave of developments in soft-tissue prostheses.

The scope of this influence is considerable and includes areas ranging from artificial cartilage, synthetic corneal tissue and intervertebral disc repair to the emerging field of tissue engineering, in which the body's own cells are used in conjunction with polymer supports to grow replacement tissue and organs. All of these developments lie within the field of biomaterials, once a fledgling discipline but now well recognised as an area of huge social and economic importance.

An obvious example is the area of chronic wound care. The financial impact of this in the field of healthcare is enormous and increasing, a feature of an ageing population. According to US healthcare statistics, the average cost of treating an individual wound ulcer is between $5,000 and $25,000, depending on the severity and the patient's response to treatment. The situation is similar in the UK, where wound care products account for a significant proportion of the prescriptions written in general practice.

The treatment and healing of wounds, particularly chronic wounds, has entered a new era. Recent advances in wound care management and technologies pay increasing attention to the manipulation of tissue cells involved in the healing process and the understanding of the relationship of the interfacial properties of wound dressings to the biochemical aspects of the healing process. Advanced wound care products, including synthetic and biosynthetic dressings, have an important part to play in improving the progress of the healing process and the consequent well-being of patients.

If the connection between Otto Wichterle and the current principles of biomaterials science are less than obvious, the existence and undoubted success of the soft contact lens industry is very clearly the direct result of his personal innovation. Although it may be thought of as a purely commercial industry, it has not only contributed to improved standards of vision but has given rise to a vast wealth of research that has contributed both directly and indirectly to the broader areas of biomaterials understanding and development.

It was just over 50 years ago that Otto Wichterle enunciated one of the now important principles of biomaterials – that of biomimesis. As a young academic he was travelling on a train from Olomouc to Prague, sitting next to a man who was reading an ophthalmic magazine. When he noticed a large advertisement for tantalum metal prostheses for ocular implants, by his own admission he could not contain himself. He expounded to the man the folly of using metals for soft tissue replacement, saying that in his opinion, instead of metal, it would be much better to invent some plastic for implants of this sort, which would be more compatible with the surrounding tissue. He made the suggestion of using slightly cross-linked hydrophilic three-dimensional polymers from which better compatibility could be expected.

As it turned out, his fellow traveller was the secretary of a commission for the application of plastics in medicine at the Czech Ministry of Health and Otto Wichterle was invited to make a presentation on the subject to the commission. He expounded what is now recognised as a biomimetic approach – that is, using the natural system as a guide to the required properties and behaviour in order that the prosthesis mimics the functions of host as closely as possible.

So was born – as a result of an accidental encounter – the concept of a tissue-compatible hydrophilic gel network, formulated to have optimum compatibility towards living tissue, which should have an elasticity similar to that of the tissue with which it is to come in contact, should be permeable to the relevant water soluble, low molecular weight metabolites, should be chemically and biochemically stable under physiological conditions and should not contain any extractable irritants.

In the presentation of these principles to the commission there was just one snag. At that time Otto Wichterle had not worked in the field of biomaterials and was simply developing, with remarkable prescience, concepts that he had begun to formulate in the course of his fortuitous train journey. So it was that when asked for samples of these materials, Wichterle was forced to admit that materials with such properties did not yet exist. The commission members became quite hostile on finding that the discussion was based on hypothetical materials. His later reflection that it was this opposition that drove him to turn theory into reality is absolutely characteristic of his scientific (and political life). His research was characterised by vision and the determination to turn that vision into reality.

He began work, almost single handed, on the development of the soft biomimetic gels that were his brainchild. In the course of his activities he pursued the thought that the materials would be particularly good for ocular prostheses and in so doing came up with the novel concept – now so widely used – of a soft contact lens that sat comfortably on the cornea and gave visual correction. None of the existing plastics fabrication techniques were applicable to the emerging gel materials, so he developed his own in unusual circumstances that provide a sort of cameo of his ability to use opposition as an incentive to succeed.

In 1958 he was dismissed from his academic position at Prague University and effectively put under house arrest by Communist Party officials on the grounds that he was 'politically unreliable'. Otto Wichterle was not deterred. He carried out research in the family kitchen with the help of his wife. By the 1961 Christmas vacation, using the equivalent of a Meccano set borrowed from his children, he built a prototype of the first centrifugal casting machine – a technique still used in contact lens manufacture. The prototype lenses were used by an ophthalmologist colleague on patients in an ophthalmic clinic with great success. He later wrote: 'My wife and I produced lenses every evening. In a week we were able to produce several hundred lenses and in the first four months of 1962 we produced about 5,500 lenses.'

Despite the success of this novel device for visual correction – based on a material which, significantly, showed the excellent compatibility with the anterior eye that he had predicted from the outset – there was little belief amongst ophthalmologists and optometrists in Eastern Europe that they had any practical future. Undeterred, Otto Wichterle continued his work on these so-called 'hydrogel' materials and methods for their fabrication into medical devices, protecting his inventions with a series of patents.

News of these hydrogel contact lenses was greeted with more interest in the West and, during a break in the Cold War, licence agreements were signed with the National Patent Development Corporation of New York, which sub-licensed enabling the lens to be put into production using Otto Wichterle's novel spin-casting technique. In 1971, following extensive clinical trials, the US FDA gave regulatory approval for the distribution and use of the first hydrogel-based soft contact lenses. This not only marked the beginning of the worldwide soft contact lens industry but also the first biomimetic soft tissue biomaterial. Otto Wichterle's predictions, which have proved to be unerringly correct, have underpinned all subsequent activity in this field – not only the soft contact lens.

Despite the huge financial success of soft contact lenses, Wichterle himself was never a significant beneficiary, not least because the Czechoslovak Academy of Sciences sold the patents without his knowledge for the equivalent of a year's royalty income. There were many intriguing twists and turns in Wichterle's career, which continued to be marked by opposition and controversy whilst his invention was being exploited in the West. His work continued at the Prague Institute of Macromolecular Chemistry, where he rose to become Director.

Pursuit of personal wealth was not a driving influence in his life – in contrast to his forthright determination to express his political and scientific views. Otto Wichterle was publicly involved in the short-lived period of liberalisation often associated with Alexander Dubček. The arrival of Russian troops and tanks soon put an end to these ideas of political freedom. Wichterle was dismissed as Director of his laboratory, although allowed to remain at the Institute as a researcher. For a considerable period he was forbidden to travel and to receive visitors.

Otto Wichterle did receive national recognition in the years following the collapse of communist control of Czechoslovakia, and ultimately became President of the Academy of the Czech Republic. He lived to see his invention revolutionalise the ophthalmic industry, before his death at the age of 84 in 1998. His enunciation of the principles of biomimesis and tireless pursuit of the demonstration of these principles in the face of such opposition has influenced something of much broader importance, however. We are now seeing an important era of innovation directed to the development of biomimetic biomaterials for bodily repair and regeneration involving an extensive range of body sites. The fundamental principle of biomimesis in soft tissue biomaterials design was demonstrated by Otto Wichterle in the face of considerable opposition – given the current climate of support for healthcare research how can we not be optimistic for the future of this important area?

Muscle physiology – the value of realising you're wrong

David Jones

It is difficult. Sitting here trying to write about optimism, I am taken back 50 years to a hot day in a large room sitting amongst serried ranks of desks under examination conditions taking part in the school essay competition. The title was 'Them' and I had no idea what to write. When, later, I complained to my father he told me that it could have had something to do with the way the individual views society, which did not really help very much. Now, as a responsible adult, I had imagined that those feelings of empty frustration, of not knowing what the title meant or even less of what to say, was in the past, but, apparently, it remains as strong as ever.

The other memory of that time is of sitting at the dining room table doing, or not doing, my homework and my mother saying 'for goodness sake David, just make a start, put something, anything, down on paper'. So, unlike that 15-year-old boy, I am going to take her advice.

Thinking about it, there are not many reasons to be optimistic. I might well get swine flu, this week or next, since at the moment Birmingham is apparently the best place to do so in the UK. The Labour Government looks to be doomed; university funding seems set to be cut for the foreseeable future; the next RAE (Research Assessment Exercise), or its equivalent, is probably only about five years away and every rheumatologist I meet looks at my painful little finger and either asks if I am sure it is not gout, or laughs and says the only sure cure is to chop it off.

I suppose I could be optimistic about the advances in molecular biology and our new understanding of intracellular signalling pathways. I remember, not so long ago, a cartoon in *New Scientist* of a conference on the latest advances in insulin research. It showed a black box with insulin going in one side and 'effects' coming out the other. That was only a few years ago but we now know so much about insulin signalling with its spaghetti junction of pathways littered with initials such as IRS and Akt. What baffles me is how various physiological stimuli that produce different results all seem to use the same pathways or at least the same intermediates, G proteins, mTor etc. Why do the different pathways not get mixed up? I am not optimistic I will ever understand this.

And this seems to be the case with every rational argument I can come up with for being optimistic; there is always some doubt, some counter-argument. We may find a treatment for one disease but will we be able to afford it given the likely economic situation and the rising tide of obesity that threatens to overwhelm the health service with diabetes and cardiovascular disease? So my rational side says that I am not optimistic but, despite the doubts, I do feel optimistic, or at least cheerful. I want to carry on, not in the sense of battling against the odds, but rather with a sense of fun and enjoyment of exploring some of the questions of muscle physiology that have stimulated me for nearly 40 years.

I came into muscle physiology quite by chance because as a post-doctoral with a wife, baby and house to support I needed a job and was offered one with Richard Edwards at the Hammersmith Hospital, as a biochemist who could measure metabolites such as ATP and phosphocreatine in muscle biopsies. The great good fortune for me was that working at the Royal Post Graduate Medical School, on the Hammersmith site, was David Hill (DKH), son of the famous muscle physiologist, AV Hill, and it was DKH who gave me the opportunity of using his apparatus and seeing biochemistry in action.

Every time a muscle contracts the myosin molecules bind to actin filaments, generating force and movement, and in the process ATP is split and then regenerated from phosphocreatine, glycolysis or oxidative processes. For no other reason than 'it might be interesting', David Hill suggested we look at muscle fatigue and in particular the slowing of contraction speed and power output that is evident as 400 and 800m athletes struggle coming down the final home straight.

One reason why metabolically depleted muscle might slow is because the cross bridges may detach more slowly since binding of ATP is required for the detachment process. Unlike a rubber band or a coiled spring, the force a muscle can develop is affected by the speed of shortening so that the faster the contraction the lower the force. AV Hill in 1938 had shown that this relationship is well described by a modified hyperbola and, in 1957, Andrew Huxley demonstrated how a relatively simple two-state kinetic model of cross-bridge attachment and detachment could account for this characteristic behaviour. A slow rate of cross-bridge detachment would affect the force–velocity relationship of the muscle and this is something that could be measured.

So I began, with a number of colleagues, to try and show that the force–velocity relationship does change with fatigue. The search might have been a lot shorter had I not been working with mammalian, and specifically human, muscle, and had I not been looking at other things such as muscle pain and damage and growth during childhood and adolescence as well as with strength training. However, the upshot was that we showed in a variety of animal and human muscle preparations that there is, indeed, a change in the relationship as the muscle fatigues and slows.

The original hypothesis predicted that it would be cross-bridge detachment that was slowed, decreasing the rate at which the muscle could relax, and for a number of years we struggled to interpret the data in this way but always with a slight nagging doubt. However, as a twist in the tail, we recently carried out a series of experiments in which it became clear that it is the apparent rate of attachment that slows with fatigue, not the detachment. After the initial shock of realising that I had been wrong for the last 30 years came a sense of satisfaction, since the new explanation ties up a number of loose ends.

Does this make me optimistic? In part, yes, because I can see a way forward. I used to bore, or possibly patronise, students by drawing an analogy between fatiguing muscle and a broken-down car. With a car the first thing to do is find which system has failed: is it the transmission, the fuel supply or the electrical circuits that have gone wrong? Having solved that question, the next step is to find out why that part of the machinery has failed: a blocked fuel line or loose wire perhaps? With fatiguing muscle we have now identified the part of the machine that is failing, one particular aspect of the interaction of the myosin and actin molecules. The next phase is to find out what it is that is causing this interaction to go slow – and we have some ideas to work on.

As the clock shows that time is nearly up and the invigilator starts to stir, I hurriedly look over what I have written and realise that I have committed that cardinal sin of not answering the question. So in that annoying habit of mediocre students, I am going to try to cram all the things I missed out into the last paragraphs.

If optimism means believing that everything will turn out well, then clearly there is no rational basis for this: climate change, increasing world population, obesity, international conflicts and political unrest – all have to be set against the positive developments in science, engineering and the arts. However, on a much smaller scale I am optimistic and encouraged by the progress that can be made in my own little area of muscle physiology and, in as much as we can all make little contributions to the pool of knowledge, that pool will continue to grow.

Whatever physical privations the next few years, or tens of years, may bring, intellectual progress will continue. And it is the intellect that is at the core of what a colleague and friend of mine called the 'indomitable human spirit' that should be our true source of optimism.

Public engagement in science – leaving the ivory tower

Anthony Hilton

Throughout history the public has viewed scientists and the work they do through suspicious eyes. Perhaps a combination of the inaccessibility of the laboratory environment, coupled with an intrinsic fear of the unknown, has fuelled allegations of scientific meddling behind closed doors by boffins in lab coats. Unfortunately, rather than engage with the public to explain their activities, many scientists retreated into their ivory towers and this has done little to alleviate the public's cultural lack of trust of scientists which has developed over the years. But I think things are beginning to change …

A recent Ipsos MORI poll asked 2,000 adults 'who they would most trust' from a list of 19 professions: doctors were most trusted at 92%, followed by teachers (87%), the clergy (74%) and then scientists at

72% of those surveyed. Arguably, one characteristic shared by the top three trusted professions is the public's positive perception of each: they can visualise these individuals in their respective workplace, appreciate the purpose of their specific roles and identify the societal and often personal benefit from their activity. So where have scientists gone wrong?

Though they are familiar with hospitals, schools and places of worship, the public rarely has the opportunity to visit a working laboratory, particularly within my own subject discipline of microbiology, where health and safety and a requirement for containment exclude all but appropriately trained personnel. So at a time when microbiology is high on the public agenda – MRSA and *Clostridium difficile* infection result in hospital ward closures and swine flu has reached pandemic proportions – where does the public turn for informed and authoritative scientific opinion? The answer is usually the print and broadcast media, which unfortunately have suffered in the past from a tendency to sensationalise stories or communicate erroneous information due to a lack of consultation with the appropriate scientific expert. Nevertheless, I believe that scientific engagement, not only directly with the public but also through the media, is improving.

The results of a survey issued in 2006 by the Royal Society to determine the factors affecting science communication by scientists and engineers revealed some interesting findings. Of those surveyed, 74% reported having taken part in at least one science communication or public engagement activity in the previous 12 months, an increase of 18% over the preceding six years. Half of those who reported they had not engaged in any activity stated that they would like to spend more time engaging with the non-specialist public about science and that observing other colleagues taking part had a positive influence on getting them involved.

This is a very positive trend, potentially aided by an increased popularity amongst the public in recent years of science-based entertainment, but unfortunately there are still some barriers to science communication. A disappointing finding in the study was that 20% of scientists surveyed agreed with a statement that those who engaged with a non-science specialist audience were less well regarded by other scientists, and that public engagement was undertaken by those who were 'not good enough' for an academic career.

From my personal experience, I find this to be a weak argument. Public engagement is a form of democratic empowerment where the agenda is controlled by the non-expert; indeed, this is even more pronounced when engaging with schoolchildren, who do not pander to hierarchy or status. They ask the unexpected and often fundamental questions that can easily expose scientific vulnerability. So I would argue that it is a strength to be able to communicate effectively to a diversity of audiences, rather than to be confined to the peer-reviewed journals and conferences of a subject discipline. In addition to providing an ideal forum for scientific debate, 'outreach' activities in schools and communities present scientists as aspirational role models and I am confident that as this type of activity becomes more commonplace it will help promote the beneficial role of scientists in society.

Engaging with the non-science specialist directly through public lectures, workshops and exhibits is not always necessary or appropriate, and indeed the print and broadcast media have an important role to play in communicating science. Unfortunately, the short timescales involved in bringing a breaking story to press or air often preclude extensive consultation with all but the most willing and available scientists. I am encouraged that networks of scientists and journalists are forging strong links facilitated through learned societies and media centres, so that authoritative and accurate information is reported following appropriate consultation.

But the success of this is ultimately governed by the willingness of scientists to receive media inquiries from journalists. If we do not engage more fully with the media, as a profession, we are condemning ourselves to a future of misreporting and inaccurate generalisations which cannot be solved by wagging a knowing finger at the television from the confines of the sofa or shaking an educated head buried within the pages of the newspaper.

There may be some way to go before scientists gain the full trust of the public and challenge the doctors for the top spot, but I am enthusiastic that we are now leaving our ivory towers and moving in the right direction.

Power in action – motivating the next generation

Robert Berry

nergy excites engineers. How will we source it, deliver it and manage it? The energy landscape has experienced extraordinary change in the last few years. Key areas are growth in demand, increased diversification of supply and supplier, global security issues and the recognition of climate change challenges.

Power is fundamental to many of our daily activities and demand is growing – at an extraordinary pace in developing countries. India and China, for example, consumed only 10% of the world's energy in 1990 but this will grow to about 28% by 2030. Deregulation has enabled new players to enter the market and has increased competition. At the same time, access to sources of energy has been restricted by wars in the Gulf, oppressive pricing and manoeuvring from providers in Russia, and simply the very high prices demanded by those holding the resources. Energy is a matter of national security.

On top of all this, there is climate change – the realisation that we are damaging our children's chances of survival unless we act to reduce carbon and other emissions. So, you might ask, why is this something to be optimistic about?

I am an engineer. Engineers love problems – especially problems with lots of constraints. They keep us awake at night until we see a way through.

At Aston University we have a number of activities that are leading the way in this field. Our bio-energy research groups have been working for over 20 years to develop efficient techniques to convert biomass into energy and we recently established the European Bioenergy Research Institute. The Institute is pioneering new techniques for the production of heat and power from even broader ranges of materials – and at the same time providing for the sequestration of up to 25% of the carbon from the process. Universities in the Midlands are collaborating with one another and with local industries to develop a vision for the region – Birmingham 2026 – that we believe will provide substantial amounts of power and provide new energy sources in the form of hydrogen for transport.

We are incredibly fortunate to live in the UK, a windy cluster of islands surrounded by thousands of miles of relentless wave motion, yet still rich in coal deposits allowing for security and diversification. The UK is enormously rich in the intellectual capability and vision of its researchers, the maturity and forward thinking of its energy providers and the commitment to the future of energy provision of its government. This is the place to be, and this challenge we face is enormously exciting.

Other engineering disciplines have critical roles to play in this future– supply chain management and logistics, mathematics and computing and electronic engineering. Expertise in complex systems is needed to help navigate, interpret and exploit the large amounts of data from these vast energy networks, whilst sustainable construction will help us focus on intelligent buildings designed to reduce our energy demands in the first place.

The key transformation I see here is in forcing multidisciplinary collaboration. The challenges we face are on a huge scale – we must work together.

A few months ago I was the lucky beneficiary of a guided tour of the Ratcliffe power station near Nottingham. We began our tour with the massive coal pits, then followed the path of this fuel into the grinders and the boilers, then on to the turbines. Along the way we saw the flue gas desulphurisation system that produces commercial quality gypsum as a by-product whilst preventing discharge of 92% of the sulphur dioxide into the atmosphere.

On the way out, just glancing overhead I noticed three relatively small wires coming out of the main plant – three wires carrying 500 megawatts of electricity. Those wires translate (after much transformation, of course) into the holes we see in our wall sockets. And that is when it hit me: most people see just those three wires as three holes in the wall for them to plug their televisions or toasters into, but hiding behind that wall socket is something quite wondrous. The scale of a place like Ratcliffe is daunting, as is its commitment to safety, efficiency, continuity and the environment. There is an excitement to the place that is not just due to the two gigawatts of power coursing through the building. It is the sheer range of engineering activities that is so staggering: complex supply chain management, dynamic complex systems optimisation, electromechanical operations, complex chemical processes, instrumentation and control theory … the list goes on.

If young people could see this spectrum of engineering opportunities that lie behind those three wires I really do think it would inspire many into a career in energy engineering. Motivating the next generation of engineers must be one of our challenges as well.

Almost 50 years ago, science and engineering in the US was presented with this challenge: 'We choose to go to the Moon.' It transformed science and engineering across the US – especially in the state of California. The challenge for our time is more fundamental and actually more compelling: 'We will sustain mankind on Earth.' Energy engineering lies at the heart of that endeavour. We can and we will do this, and I am optimistic that the Midlands will be a beacon of innovation in its achievement.

Looking forward – new challenges, new opportunities

Rachel Edwards

A few days ago one of the professors from the department retired. Over coffee break we were given a talk about his career and the research he had done, and were entertained by the stories about fighting for lab space (something which is still true today) and trying to come up with new ideas. But the one thing that struck those of us new to academia was probably his comment about funding, and starting out with close to 100% success rate when applying for money to do his research. It is really not like that any more, with even the retiring academic suffering over the last few years.

It would be easy to get bogged down and upset by lack of funding. We need it to progress our research, to produce the data to publish papers, and hence to get out of probation. We need funding to be available so we have the time to do these experiments, rather than spending all our time writing the applications!

But is it all so bad? Sure, we are spending more time working on research grant applications, but a lot of the other things we do now are so much easier than when the retiring academic started out. Take lectures as an example. Whilst the students still appreciate the pace forced upon the lecturer by writing on the blackboard, when we want to show complex graphs we can use PowerPoint presentations and multimedia shows. We are no longer limited to just the graphs we can sketch, which is extremely helpful for those without much artistic talent …

Technology is also helping with the experiments, giving more time compared with those retiring academics who started their research by slaving over a dim oscilloscope screen, dutifully copying down the numbers and plotting things on paper.

My research is split into two areas, applied physics (such as using science to help stop rail disasters due to cracks in railway tracks) and fundamental measurements of new magnetic materials, studying how the speed of sound in them changes when we reduce the temperature and put them in a magnetic field. When I started this second part of my research, I inherited a rack full of equipment, last used about ten years ago, and developed many years before then. The idea was to measure the speed of sound by sending two pulses through the sample, and varying the time between them (by hand!) to try to get them to overlap. Hmmm!

I sat down and looked at the equipment and tried to work it out. Most of it was developed within the department by people who have since retired or gone on to important jobs running the university, so there were not any manuals. The papers I read gave some idea of what to expect, but nowhere was there a list saying 'press this button to get a signal'. After a bit more thought the answer was obvious. Buy new stuff! Fortunately I had a little bit of funding to get started, so I went with the power of USB and bought a new oscilloscope and a new computer, and installed LabVIEW …

Some days later, with the help of a few undergraduate project students, most of the old equipment was redundant. At the press of a button on the computer screen I could take the data required, analyse it, record the data and also the analysis output to hard disk, and start to plot a graph.

Experiments which had previously taken weeks were now possible in days, leaving plenty more time for writing those pesky grant applications. And it is similar in the applied physics area. Ideas which were suggested 50 years ago are now feasible, with the increases in computer power and speed.

So where am I now? I am still in my probationary period, and still playing with setting things up, but I am having fun. Maybe it is not as easy a job as it used to be, but it is still a wonderful area to be working in. And funding? Well, even though the UK and US research funding is suffering, there are other opportunities appearing. The EU recently started its own European Research Council, offering two grants: the starting grant, designed to help new academics develop a team, and the advanced grant for the more experienced academics, both offering up to five years of funding to allow the academic to concentrate on research.

The more schemes such as this, the better, as they allow new academics to spend the time doing the research we need to become known and move up the career ladder. Me? I was very lucky and got one of the starting grants, by mixing a bit of physics and a bit of engineering.

And the other thing to be optimistic about, compared with when the retiring academic started, is that it is now possible to make it as a female physicist. The department I am working in has been awarded Juno Champion status by the Institute of Physics, and has approximately the same percentage of females throughout all levels, from undergraduate to professor. We now all have role models to look up to and know that there is a fair chance for success.

So, while times are undeniably difficult, with even the best new academics having problems gaining funding and worrying about progression through probation, maybe it is not the worst time to be starting a new academic career.

Looking back – sonochemistry and the cross-fertilisation of ideas

Tim Mason

As I begin to consider retirement I also reflect upon the way that science, and in particular scientific research, has changed over my working life and how it will develop in the future. This article gives me the chance to express my worries about the current situation and my optimism about one or two things that appear to be happening to overcome them.

Like many others, when I think of scientific research I worry about the current trends towards specialisation. It is to be expected that research should be compartmentalised into generic fields such as chemistry, physics, mathematics and engineering. My degree choice of chemistry has traditionally been subdivided into organic, inorganic and physical, but I am concerned about the increasing number of sub-subdivisions arising within these areas, such as molecular electronics and computational chemistry. This restrictive specialisation closes some of the doors to broader scientific understanding.

It is my contention that over-specialism is wasteful of the potential of graduates themselves because they have little knowledge in other areas, and the opportunity to contribute to cross-disciplinary research is seldom, if ever, presented. There are two approaches to solving this problem. The first involves modifying basic science education in order to produce more rounded scientists. The second accepts the current position of specialisation and looks for ways in which we can open up new avenues into which our scientists can move and diversify. A combination of these two would be ideal.

The first approach is to bring in more general science courses to 16-year-old students rather than a specialist set of separate science subjects. The International Baccalaureate offers this and is becoming more popular in schools in the UK. It could provide a good model for science education in the future. The second approach is designed for existing science specialists, and involves building them into multidisciplinary teams organised around a common research theme. In such a team, each member can contribute his or her own specialism, but by taking part in team meetings and especially in discussions about research strategy the individual will also exchange knowledge and information with the others. This means that everyone catches glimpses of the breadth of their common theme and is inspired to diversify. This model is what gives me the greatest hope for the future, for I have seen it operate extremely successfully within my own Sonochemistry Applied Research Centre.

This research started 30 years ago when I was appointed as a lecturer in chemistry at what was then called Lanchester Polytechnic and is now Coventry University. The department I entered was Chemistry & Metallurgy and whilst wandering around the metallurgy laboratories I chanced upon colleagues using ultrasonic baths for the surface cleaning of metal samples. At that time I did not know much about ultrasound, acoustic cavitation or the energies involved, but my research up to that point had been involved in studies of the factors that influence the rates of chemical reactions. So it was a bit of a step into the unknown for me to begin investigations into whether this 'new' energy used for cleaning might also be used to accelerate reactions. Thus began my long-term research interest in what has now become known as sonochemistry.

Many of the publications in the early years of the subject reported improved synthetic procedures, predominantly in heterogeneous systems and particularly for organometallic reactions. Nowadays it has expanded to take in disciplines outside of chemical synthesis, including medicine (therapeutic ultrasound, drug delivery), materials science (nanotechnology, encapsulation), food processing (extraction of natural materials, sterilisation) and environmental protection (water treatment, biofuels). Evidence for this breadth of interests can be found in the contents of the journal *Ultrasonics Sonochemistry* and in the biennial meetings of the European Society of Sonochemistry. The resulting cross-fertilisation of ideas leads to a rapid growth of interdisciplinary research and gives me the greatest optimism about the future.

My own team contains researchers from the fields of biology, chemistry, environmental science, food technology, materials science and pharmacology. This gives the sort of combination of different backgrounds that allows the development of new ideas for research across the boundaries of their individual disciplines. A significant bonus arising from this interaction is that all the participants approach sonochemistry from different points of view, which I think makes the subject more generally understood.

This was brought home to me quite recently when we exhibited at the Royal Society Summer Science Exhibition. Our exhibit, 'The Power of Sound', involved lots of preparation, design and thought about to how to present the work in an understandable, digestible and stimulating way. Every member of the team participated and each talked about the wide range of work within the field of sonochemistry. The response from the exhibition visitors was excellent and we came away knowing that the combination of disciplines working together, and scientific discussion within the team, had helped to make the presentation of our research more accessible.

So this is what makes me feel so positive about sonochemistry. I think it provides an ideal model for linking scientific disciplines to expand scientific knowledge through opening the closed doors of specialist science.

The view from my window – just a patch of weeds

Chris McCabe

Next to the glass and metal door I open every morning on my way into work lies a small patch of weeds. It is sandwiched between a car park, a stretch of gravel and the fresh, red brick of the research institute. The size of a couple of family cars, sloping gently away, bordered on the far side by a wall and a sheer drop. A no man's land that did not appear on any maps, that was not in the plans, that did not get factored in when the biomedical institute was carefully drawn up and meticulously constructed.

Above the rectangle of weeds, a round fluorescent light burns endlessly through the summer and the winter, through the day and through the night. No one knows how to turn it off. There is no switch and no sensor. The building is complicated, the receptionist tells me. The lights are part of a system, the building manager confirms. Something would have to be re-programmed, a technician ventures. And still the light burns on.

A few months ago, in the shock of a January which actually turned out to be cold, two men arrived. Over the course of a day, while we stared into microscopes watching human cells grow and divide, they bounced their shovels off the freezing soil, their breath fixed in the air, their cheeks red with the effort. By the time I left the Institute, the warm air of the laboratory seeping out of my clothes, the weeds were gone. Green had become brown. The battle had been won. I cycled home in the dark, through blackened playing fields and along orange roads, thinking about that small patch of weeds. Cyclists in the dark; a wasteland amongst tarmac.

The following day, the men were back. Men like my father. Solid, stoic, refusing to be beaten by the temperature. They had arrived with wheelbarrows. The cold dry air held the wet scent of wood. As we sifted through data, muttered about progress, they took turns shovelling bark chippings over the area, four inches deep, flattened down with a roller. They had brought order where there was chaos. Control where there was anarchy. It was a form of botanic tyranny. The by-product of one species of plant used to suppress a rebellion of other unwanted species.

And so it continues, day after day. Many people cannot look at a stretch of grass without wanting to dig it up. It haunts them at night, tracks them down in the early hours, tunnels itself in and festers. An area of land not actually doing anything. The final crime of the twenty-first century. Not to be doing.

Spring took an age to arrive. The blackened playing fields became grey and hazy. Improbable irises, slender and frail, burst through the frozen concrete soil. Birds returned from their travels and found their voices again. The air-conditioned research laboratory remained resolutely at 21°C. The fluorescent light continued to shine. And fragile shoot after fragile shoot began to explore their way through the corpses of trees, the layer of bark chippings pressing relentlessly down on them. Soon, a thin carpet of tendrils, striving, yearning, fighting. Mute organisms reaching for the pale spring sun, stretching up and out, mammals emerging from hibernation.

A man with a shovel arrived. Half an hour of half-hearted labour and he had turned the layer of bark chippings over. We had barely thawed our lab reagents. Then he lit a cigarette and climbed back into his van.

I watched the patch over the coming weeks. The weeds tried again, got a little further that time, before the same man returned. Another few weeks, the same result. As I enter the building some mornings I picture a university administrator with a post-it note stuck to the side of his monitor. It says 'No Surrender'. Every few weeks he picks up his phone or types an email. Somewhere the University Estates section registers the fact that a small patch of unwanted ground adjacent to its biomedical research building might be fighting back.

Above, and looking down from my laboratory, that patch of weeds makes me insanely optimistic.

Afterword

For some time, I'd thought about publishing. The revolution with print-on-demand and web-based technologies has changed the game. In the cold damp light of a winter day in early 2009, I speculated that much could now be done with insouciance, a laptop on the kitchen table and a lifetime's fascination with how scientists work, how seemingly ordinary men and women as part of their daily routine engage with extraordinary matters and, to paraphrase the mathematician Ian Stewart, defend us from believing what we want to.

An initial idea to provide written demonstration of the value created by scientists has, through the efforts of many people, morphed into a fledgling not-for-profit multimedia publishing venture, Linus Publishing. The book you're reading now, *The New Optimists*, is its first offering.

The scientists who feature here, over half of whom are professors, over two-thirds working in medical and life sciences, have written "*this most exhilarating of books*", as Jenny Uglow describes it in her Foreword. I thank every one of these remarkable men and women.

In the Foreword, Jenny has done the scientists proud, creating such a lyrically pertinent context for their work.

Thanks are also due to Keith Richards, whose light-touch editing of the essays themselves, and his imaginative structure for the book as a whole, adds to the impact of the essays both individually and collectively.

The book you're now reading simply wouldn't exist without an experienced publisher on board. Right at the outset, Etica's Julian Roskams saw something catching in providing a means for these scientists to tell their tale. It's his efforts that have translated all the ideas of all of us, scientist and non-scientist, into paper and print. His cheerfully calm professionalism has never wavered even when I have been unreasonably demanding.

There has been much other work behind the scenes. Fiona Alexander, Steve Bedser, Nick Booth, Chris Buckham, David Edmonds, Kevin Johnson, Alison Murray and Mike Smith have, in their free time, responded to my calls, my texts, my emails and from time to time have met, often over my kitchen table, to make things happen.

"What is the use of a book," thought Alice, "without pictures and conversations?" As Jenny Uglow says in her Foreword, this collection of essays "*is itself a kind of conversation*". Pictures in a book, however, present a costly option. But we have these intriguing, inspiring images on the book cover from many-times Wellcome Image Award winner, local photomicrographer Spike Walker. He readily agreed to designer Jonathan Doyle using them, as did the Wellcome Trust. On the back cover, we have a derived image of dopamine, one of the birth of a daphnia; the spine has an image of human brain cells; on the front cover are the images of urea, the moment before a (failed) human IVF, a spider's mandibles and liver blood vessels (double injected with two pigments to show the complexity of the blood supply). All of these are visually delicious examples of how science enables us literally to see the world quite differently.

As you've read here, many people have given of their time and energies. But there are some bills that can't be avoided, some favours that go too far beyond the reasonable. Aston University and the University of Birmingham (College of Medical and Dental Sciences) have sponsored this early stage of the project, and I thank them very much indeed for their generous support.

acknowledgments

As well as this book, we're creating web and e-book versions and, funding permitting, multimedia spin-offs about aspects of the scientists' work. Plus, there are plans afoot for our next publication about science, about its value and impact on us all, as well as its beauty and excitement.

Much can indeed be done with insouciance, a laptop on the kitchen table … and a wonderful coterie of over 100 people. I salute them all.

Kate Cooper

Linus Publishing

May 2010